Hope with OCD

Dedication

To Kevin, Charlotte and Samantha

The unconditional love we share for each other is the wind beneath my wings.

My mum – thank you for always listening.

Chris,
I hope this book lives up to its title for you.
Lots of love and Hope
Lynn x.

Hope with OCD

A self-help guide to obsessive compulsive disorder for parents, carers and friends of sufferers

Lynn Crilly

With a Foreword by Dr Russell Delderfield

BOOKS
Hammersmith Health Books
London, UK

First published in 2018 by Hammersmith Health Books – an imprint of
Hammersmith Books Limited
4/4A Bloomsbury Square, London WC1A 2RP, UK
www.hammersmithbooks.co.uk

The information contained in this book is for educational purposes only. It is
the result of the study and the experience of the author. Whilst the information
and advice offered are believed to be true and accurate at the time of going to
press, neither the author nor the publisher can accept any legal responsibility or
liability for any errors or omissions that may have been made or for any adverse
effects which may occur as a result of following the recommendations given
herein. Always consult a qualified medical practitioner if you have any concerns
regarding your health.

British Library Cataloguing in Publication Data: A CIP record of this book is
available from the British Library.

Print ISBN 978-1-78161-145-6
Ebook ISBN 978-1-78161-146-3

Commissioning editor: Georgina Bentliff
Designed and typeset by: Julie Bennett, Bespoke Publishing Ltd.
Cover design by: Julie Bennett, Bespoke Publishing Ltd.
Cover image: Shutterstock.com/Butterfly Hunter
Index: Dr Laurence Errington
Production: Helen Whitehorn, Path Projects Ltd.
Printed and bound by: TJ International Ltd.

Contents

About the author

Lynn Crilly is an award-winning counsellor, author and mother of twin girls. After finding one of her twin daughters, Samantha, was struggling with OCD and anorexia nervosa, and having followed the conventional therapy routes to no avail, Lynn took the decision to follow her gut instincts and rehabilitate Samantha herself. She subsequently developed her unique form of counselling to support sufferers and their families going through similar experiences.

Lynn continues to work with families battling mental health issues every day at her clinic in Surrey. She is admired for her passion and understanding – something she attributes to the strength and loyalty of her family and friends, with whom she spends as much time as possible.

Acknowledgements

First and foremost, I would like to say a BIG thank you to my wonderful husband, Kevin, who has always given me his unconditional love and support. His unquestioning belief in me has given me the strength to achieve all I have so far…. I love you more with every new day.

To our beautiful twin daughters, Charlotte and Samantha, I am so proud of the gorgeous young ladies you have become and love you both very much!

A big thank you to Callum and Jay for loving my girls unconditionally and making my family complete – love you both loads.

Much love to my mum and dad, who have always been there for me with the kettle on and ready to listen, with their constant love and support.

My brother Steve and sister-in-law Sue, thank you for being there.

A special thank you to Kate, Wendy, Jill, Gerry, Leanne, Hannah, Dionne, Kyra, Michelle, Shauna, Neil and all my friends who continue to love me unconditionally; your friendship is a rare and valued gift.

A warm thank you to our wonderful GPs, past and present, Dr John Dalzell and Dr Sarah Benney, who over the years have given us as a family and me as a professional their unreserved support.

Thank you to all my clients both past and present who have

put their trust and belief in me and my work. This has enabled me to help and support them to make the positive changes needed in their lives and in doing so, changed mine.

Once again, I have been incredibly privileged to have been supported by so many wonderful people from all walks of life, who have all trusted and believed in me enough to make a contribution to *Hope with OCD*. I thank you all.

Lastly, and by no means least, thank you to my lovely publisher Georgina Bentliff (Hammersmith Health Books) for being so supportive, open minded and a total pleasure to work with.

Once again, a big thank you to all the mentioned above and the many others who have helped and supported me over the years. Without each and every one of you, I know I would not be who and where I am today, both personally and professionally; for this I will always be grateful.

Foreword

As I go about my research into men's eating disorders, I am often struck by the overlap between some of the experiences that people report about struggling with disordered eating and battling obsessive compulsive disorder. My interest in OCD is, therefore, a natural curiosity emerging from this observation. As such, I was delighted to be given the opportunity to read this new perspective on the topic.

Anyone searching for information about OCD will know that there is a wealth of material out there that can be accessed. Websites, books, leaflets and videos can all be useful in helping you to find out more, improve understanding and aid recovery, but none are quite like this book.

Let me tell you what Lynn's text is not. It is not a clinical guide. Nor is it an impersonal, detached account of the condition... not that there is anything wrong with either of these, of course. Medical guides are not only useful but necessary.

Now let me tell you what this book is. It is a unique blend of four core elements. This powerful and innovative consideration of OCD deftly weaves together the following: accessible information about the nature of OCD and its presentation; unbiased exploration of several recovery approaches; practitioner experience of these methods; and personal reflections of how these treatments have made a difference to individuals. In addition to these four elements, Lynn's work has heart and honesty. Her own family's healing runs through the book, illustrating the possibilities of recovery without glibly presenting this as an 'easy' or linear process.

As well as being a good read, there is real intent to offer options. One core message that runs throughout is the importance of freedom – being free to try different ways to find recovery. This makes sense because OCD presents differently in each individual, and, as such, people need to think about a range of different solutions, treatments and therapies. The trick is not to give up if some standard treatment does not prove effective. As Lynn believes, you should persist and find something that works for you.

This leads us to another core message: hope. Lynn's professional and personal experiences have a genuine message of hope, and this permeates everything that you read here. The book shows that recovery really is possible, and, most importantly, that there is more than one way to get there. Caring, love, awareness and clear information are key to tackling the pervasive and damaging influence of OCD – and this book has these in abundance.

Dr Russell Delderfield
University of Bradford, UK

An unwanted intruder

By Samantha Crilly

I lay there asleep, in peace on my bed
Avoiding waking to confront the demon in my head
Losing myself in my beautiful dreams
Feeling free, well, for what it seems
I wake and feel the constraint around me
Face to face with the monster that has found me
Reeling out a list of rules I should follow
Each with a meaning that seems so hollow
But as I do one, it makes me do more
If I ever missed one, it would yell as it saw
I obeyed every rule, scared of upsetting it
It knew it could own me, and I was letting it
Drained and tired from doing what it desired
I was the personal slave that it had hired
So consumed in the rituals I had to do
I was losing everything else that once was true
My freedom was jailed
Imprisoned in a hell I hailed
Watching my loved ones fall apart beside me
It was time I set light to the fire inside me
This presence was my enemy, not my friend
And a relationship that I needed to end
I burnt my bridges and cut my ties
I ripped it apart and said my goodbyes
I have the freedom now to live my life and be free
But over my shoulder, it's always watching me
Its shadow lingers at a distance
And whispers to me in its persistence
But I stand strong, you will stay a ghost, and I will walk past
your existence.

To cut a long story short...

Anyone looking at us 12 years ago would have assumed from the outside that we were a perfectly 'normal' family: my husband Kevin and I, together with our beautiful twin daughters, Charlotte and Samantha, seemed to have everything anyone could possibly wish for, and more. We were in a really good place in our lives, glued together by the strong foundations of our marriage and two happy, healthy girls. Of course, we had our ups and downs like most couples and life threw challenges our way, but we always worked together to overcome them and move forward, trying carefully to balance our scaffolding business and family life, just like any other working parents. We were doing okay... or so we thought.

Our picture-perfect little world fell apart when Samantha was diagnosed with the early stages of anorexia nervosa at the start of her teenage years. We had had very little experience of mental illness at that time and were not prepared for what was to come. Looking back, Samantha had always exhibited a vivid imagination, creating unlikely and outlandish scenarios from a very early age, though to her, these imaginings seemed very real, leading her to repeatedly check door locks, window locks, toilet seats and light switches. We had no knowledge at all of OCD when the girls were young and dismissed these peculiarities as being Samantha's quirky traits, her uniqueness of character. It was something we neither encouraged, discouraged nor over-analysed – it was just Samantha being Samantha. Now, with the diagnosis of anorexia nervosa we were equally and naively unaware of the condition or the precise help or treatment needed for our lovely daughter as we watched her spiral so quickly out of control and into the grip of something which affected each of us individually and our family as a whole. I had no idea how to deal with eating disorders at that time, but my husband and I believed that if we entrusted Samantha's health to the 'system' she would get better – we had no reason to think otherwise at that point. However, in hindsight, and knowing what I know now, had we had the knowledge and understanding to enable us to identify and address the OCD in Samantha's childhood, I feel we might have been in a stronger position to intervene at a much earlier stage with the eating disorder. Who knows, we might have even nipped it in the bud…

Over the next three devastating years we tried everything we could to get her the help she so desperately needed, from our local (very supportive) GP to both NHS and private clinics and therapists, but sadly nothing appeared to be working for Samantha. As things progressed from bad to worse, we all felt completely helpless as we watched our beautiful daughter become a shadow of her former self, the trauma fragmenting the family with each of us suffering in our own particular way.

Like any parent, I wanted to do the best I could to help my daughter to recover both mentally and physically and support my family to have a better understanding of her illness. I read many books and scoured the internet for as much information and guidance as I could get my hands on, but could not find anything that I or my family could truly relate to or which gave me any real hope that there might be a light at the end of the tunnel for Samantha and for us as a family. It seemed to me that we were all feeling around in the dark, not knowing what we were supposed to say or do. Every website, book or support group I found seemed to focus mainly on the actual person experiencing the illness and not the family, friends or carers who

I felt needed help and support just as much as the sufferer. I desperately needed answers and wanted to reach out to others – anybody with a genuine understanding of what was happening to us – to help us stop Samantha's condition in its tracks, but to no avail. There was nothing. I was also deeply troubled by the fact that my husband, my other daughter, Charlotte, and I were at times all made to feel that Samantha's illness had somehow been our fault. We were living in what felt like a pressure cooker, thinking we were going to explode at any given moment and constantly scrutinising ourselves, which in itself was only adding to the overall destruction. It seemed as though there was a great deal of blame being flung around when answers were thin on the ground and those closest to the sufferer were often an easy target.

Having exhausted all the options available to us, the painful truth was that Samantha was not getting any better – if anything, she was becoming more and more unwell, both physically and mentally. So, in a moment of desperation and with my family falling apart, as radical as it might have been, I let my intuition guide me and took the decision to rehabilitate her myself. Thankfully, with the full support of our GP, the school and our friends and family, I was able to dedicate myself completely to Samantha, injecting positive thinking, love and hope, whilst trying to show her a life outside of the eating disorder, never giving up on my belief that she would get better no matter how difficult the situation became. I worked closely with Samantha's school, knowing it was important to keep her in as normal an environment as possible, and everyone involved worked as a team throughout the recovery process.

There were no set rules to follow, no specific path to guide me, but by committing myself fully to Samantha's recovery and trying my utmost to understand things from her troubled perspective, I slowly encouraged her to start communicating with me. She began sharing her distorted and, at times, highly irrational views of her world and her innermost thoughts, her head engaged in constant battle with itself. Patience, love and open-mindedness were paramount, not just for Samantha, but for the family as a unit, ensuring the lines of communication were left open at all times between us. We needed all to be on the same page, so we could help Samantha and heal together. It turned out to be the steepest learning curve I could have ever imagined. Looking back, it was quite a controversial thing to do I suppose, but at the time my instinct told me it was the right and only way to get my daughter better as nothing appeared to have had an impact so far. Step by step over the following year or so, Samantha slowly found her way back to us and began to leave behind the eating disorder that had had such a profound and devastating effect, not only on her but on all of us. However, we were not completely out of the woods yet and I have to admit I still had my suspicions that there was something else, some underlying factor that was stalling Samantha's recovery.

She was still very vulnerable at this time. Being exposed to outside influences, including an intense relationship with a friend who was suffering from OCD, had a negative impact on her progress. Samantha inadvertently began to copy some of the friend's traits and habits relating to food, which was both her weakness and the catalyst that led to her subsequently suffering a major setback as OCD began to manifest itself in place of her eating disorder. Control was once again the core element for her – although she was more out of control than she realised. That is the illusion with mental illnesses such as OCD and eating disorders – the sufferer believes that they have full control, when in reality it is completely the opposite and the mental illness has complete control over them. Food, and everything associated with it, was pivotal in Samantha's mental illness, so it seemed a fairly predictable and inevitable progression that OCD would come to the forefront once again and latch onto this weakness, making her recovery even more difficult and challenging. This time Samantha was more comfortable opening up to me and began to explain why she felt a certain way and why she had to carry out certain acts and rituals, which helped me to accept and understand the OCD much more clearly this time around. With Samantha's desire and determination to get better, we ploughed on together, a united team against OCD, gently rebuilding our family life into a new and stronger version of what it had previously been.

Kevin, my husband, has never really understood mental illness, and has never pretended to, but the pressure and the enormity of it all took its toll on us briefly at the height of Samantha's illness, to the point that I once asked him to leave. Thankfully he ignored my request and stayed, continuing to provide his powerful and unconditional love and support, without which we could never have survived. He used to think Samantha was intentionally behaving as she did for attention, but now he readily accepts things for what they are, supporting Samantha unconditionally, even though sometimes, he struggles to get his head around her quirky ways of thinking.

Samantha's twin sister, Charlotte, has also been pivotal in her recovery and now works alongside me at my practice, with an empathy that can only come from first-hand experience. She has forfeited pieces of her own life so that Samantha could be given the full-on care that she needed and the bond between my two girls is now unbelievably strong. Their mutual respect for one another, as a result of the journey they have shared, is testament to that.

I have learnt through all of this, the importance of constant communication, patience, non-judgement, unconditional love and most of all HOPE. I have also learnt that in fact there is no such thing as the 'perfect' family. Trying to be perfect is not only unrealistic, it can be dangerous.

Some time after Samantha's recovery, I was contacted by the mother of a 17-year-old girl who was suffering from an eating disorder. She asked me if I could help as they were finding, as we had, that none of the conventional routes was making any difference. Encouraged by my husband, I approached their situation just as I had Samantha's, looking beyond her illness to the person within and giving her and her family the unconditional and non-judgemental support that I realised from our experience had been so beneficial. Having been able to help her, and her family, successfully, I made the decision to build my own counselling practice based on everything I had read, learnt and experienced from our own journey with Samantha. I then went on to do some studying of my own, including training as a Master of NLP (neuro-linguistic programming). I was keen to work with other sufferers and their families, giving them the combination of unreserved support and complete lack of judgement that my own experience had taught me was vital. I tentatively opened my doors to people from all walks of life, struggling to deal with mental illness, be it the sufferer or a supportive loved one. My little successes were never shouted from the rooftops but from then on people seemed to find me through recommendation and word of mouth. I am now contacted on a daily basis by frantic and frightened parents, carers and siblings, all of whom have concerns about children as young as nine years old from all over the country, most just wanting to talk to me, desperate for a glimmer of hope. I now help people suffering with OCD, eating disorders, anxiety, depression and low self-esteem. The way I interact with my clients may seem a little unorthodox to some; however, I feel it is important to get to know the person as a whole rather than just seeing them through the lens of their illness, and working alongside the family rather than with just one person helps to build a united front against the illness. No two people who enter my office are ever the same and all experience the issues in a way that is unique to them; hence, the way I approach their treatment is similarly unique to each client. I am learning about each individual case as it naturally unfolds so I can give as much time and attention as we need both in and outside our sessions to build a mutual trust within our relationship which enables me to be one step ahead of the illness, in turn facilitating a quicker and more effective recovery for all concerned; we may, for example, do puzzles together while we chat, or make jewellery or do other arts and crafts projects. The atmosphere tends to be much less intense than the traditional image of the patient-therapist relationship, and can even be fun! I have certainly learnt a lot from working with people in this way, and I focus on maintaining a positive environment, so from the minute they walk in my clients feel comfortable and at ease; from the very start they know they can get better and that they are in control of their own recovery.

I also respond at an emotional level rather than a clinical one to the things they tell me. I do not always get it right, and I do not pretend to; occasionally there may be the need for additional assistance and input from other avenues; but my practical and down-to-earth approach has earned me the endearing handle of 'Fairy Godmother'.

So here I am, many years later. If you had told me over 10 years ago that I would be doing what I am doing today I would not have believed you. Nor could I have foreseen that our future as a family would be so much healthier and happier; our dynamics have changed in a way I did not think possible. During these rewarding years I have had the privilege of working with some wonderful people and their families, each and every one of them unique. Whilst I have been able to support and guide them through their journeys, I too have learnt from them. My clients have said that they find my practical and down-to-earth approach really refreshing and even compared me to the therapist in the film *The King's Speech* on more than one occasion! His methods were unconventional and unorthodox – but they got results. I never expected my practice to expand to the scale it has, but through this I have been able to share my ever-growing knowledge of all kinds of mental illness and help clients to find the best route towards recovery, not just for the sufferer but for those close to them.

My ever-increasing client list highlighted just how little emotional support or real empathy there was available for the carers, friends and families of those suffering from mental illness, and having had first-hand experience of the destruction it can cause within the family unit I felt compelled to write my first book (*Hope with Eating Disorders*, published in 2012). I was keen to share what I had learnt from our journey with Samantha in the hope that it would bring some guidance, comfort, strength and hope to others. Outwardly it was impossible to identify families who were going through similar experiences, yet when I spoke openly about what we had experienced within our family, I learnt that most people I knew were struggling with something behind closed doors. They had been too afraid to talk about it for fear of stigma or judgement, which sadly still surrounds mental health issues, even in today's society where a staggering one in four of us will experience or suffer from some form of mental illness at any one time. It was then I realised how widespread issues like self-harm, anxiety, depression, OCD and eating disorders were and how confusing the wealth of information available on these subjects could be to the reader. Despite many high-profile initiatives by the Government and various celebrities making mental health awareness a target, there are still countless people of all ages suffering in silence, in need of help and support, and many loved ones, friends and carers confused and unsure of how to help them.

Looking back, although Samantha had left most of her issues behind, she never truly felt comfortable in her own skin until recently, when she reignited her love for drama and the arts. Following this, we have watched her grow into a beautiful, confident and vibrant young lady, pursuing a passion that allows her to express herself. Her passion and desire for life have been strengthened by the encouragement of her supportive and loving boyfriend, Jay. Charlotte also has a wonderful, understanding fiancé, Callum, who has been on this journey with us since the beginning, so I am hugely relieved – being happy and healthy is all I have ever wanted for both of my girls.

Which brings us to *Hope with OCD*…

Having experienced at first hand some of what you are going through, my main aim in writing this new book is to help you identify and understand the symptoms of OCD as early as you possibly can, which in turn will enable early intervention with the appropriate treatment. Both of these are paramount for a quicker and more effective recovery. I try to answer some of the questions that I am asked frequently, and my objective is to give you, the reader, the hope and belief that you have the strength and courage not only to support and guide your child/friend/loved-one through these turbulent waters, but to be able to see them safely to the other side, where they, and indeed everyone closely involved with them, will be able to move forward with their lives. I would like this book to act as a road map not only for those who simply do not know where to turn for help, but also for those who would like to have a clearer understanding of the condition.

I hope to relieve you of some of the burden, confusion and pain you may be feeling, as you enter the unknown, and to arm you with as much knowledge, guidance and strength as I can, to enable you to continue your journey with courage, trusting in your own personal skills and instinct, just as I did. Remember always that communication is the key, along with unconditional love, non-judgement, patience and hope.

This book emphasises that each OCD sufferer is individual and unique; there is no 'right' or 'wrong' path to recovery. My own experience demonstrates that each family or support network must take whatever action is right for them; if one option proves ineffective, try another – never buy into the myth that OCD is incurable; never give up hope and never give up trying.

Sadly, there are no quick fixes; only perseverance and time can heal. I do not pretend to be an expert on everything and I am still learning, but I hope with the benefit of my first-hand experience, knowledge and natural empathy, I can help you, the reader (whether you are battling with OCD personally or you are a carer), work towards a happier and healthier future together. Always have hope because anything is possible... my family is living proof of that.

Over the pages that follow you will share the experiences of other carers and sufferers, and realise that the emotions you may be experiencing are normal and natural. You will be given an insight into how your loved one is thinking and feeling, with the aim of providing you with a genuine understanding of their condition. I have also included an unbiased guide to some different types of treatment available within and outside of the NHS. All the contributors and therapists are real people, but some have had their names changed to protect their identity.

Chapter 1

What is obsessive-compulsive disorder (OCD)?

In recent years, 'OCD' has become a bit of a buzzword, used frivolously as an off-the-cuff statement: 'Oh, I checked the door twice. I am soooooo OCD!' or 'Oh, I washed my hands three times. How OCD am I?' Sadly, in reality, OCD is more than that – much, much more. It is a deep-rooted, anxiety-based, debilitating and destructive mental illness that affects both the sufferers and their carers alike. Once well established, the severity of this dreadful illness, and the tormented misery it rains down on the sufferer, can destroy relationships and ruin the lives of not only the person suffering but also everyone around them.

OCD can be defined as a mental health condition that changes a person's way of thinking, their feelings, their behaviour, or – in probability – all three. This can cause the person distress and difficulty in functioning mentally, and frequently on a physical level too. Individuals who have OCD may not look as though they are ill, particularly if their symptoms are mild. However, some individuals may show more obvious and explicit physical signs. OCD can affect a wide variety of people, regardless of gender, race, age, sexuality and/or social background. The impact varies from person to person, as does the length of time it will affect each person's life. It is a serious mental illness and deserves the same attention and respect as any physical illness, yet sadly it is still often woefully misunderstood, feared and trivialised, as it cannot be seen. If we were to break one of our arms or legs, not only would a doctor know exactly how to fix it, but we would probably get a lot of sympathy and support from the people around us. With OCD, there is no such obvious cure and people around the sufferer tend to draw away, or worry that they will say or do the wrong thing. This can be frustrating for someone experiencing OCD, as they may feel that their condition has not yet been acknowledged, or that the people close to them do not care.

From my own experience, as a carer, one of the most important things I have learnt and would like to share with you at this point in the book, is that 'you have to accept what is, to enable you to understand'. You cannot apply logic to something illogical in the same way you cannot apply reason to something unreasonable and you cannot make sense out of something nonsensical. From my own experience, however difficult it may be, I would encourage you not to spend precious time and energy trying to understand the reasoning behind every action, but to look at what you can do to support your loved one, as OCD, to the carer, can have no logic, no reason and make no sense.

You may turn to the internet hoping it will help you to understand a bit more, or you may scour articles in the press on the condition; this could find you ending up even more confused and frustrated. As there is so much varied information available through various channels, it is very difficult to know what applies to you and your own situation. Within this book I aim to provide the information that I think really matters, with no agenda other than helping you to understand some of the different types of OCD, the signs to look for, and some of the options that are available to you and the sufferer.

Everyone has their own idiosyncratic habits that can become a little obsessive from time to time, and intrusive thoughts that may seem a little too dark, or fears and phobias that can have a brief impact; however, the difference from illness is that someone who is not suffering from OCD is usually able to make a very clear distinction between their thoughts and reality.

My close friend, Jill, speaks of her quirky behaviours around even numbers:

> When I fill the kettle with water to make my cup of tea, I always count to 12; then the tap goes off. I also count when I shave my legs in the shower, I can't help it ... I've tried not to but I still do! I don't really have a specific number but it is usually around 12-ish, and again as long as it's an even number I'm happy. My TV volume has to be on an even number – such as 16/18 – never on an odd number. In fact, I can't do odd numbers on anything! When I drink from a bottle of water I will count how many glugs I take and that is usually six, but as long as it's even I'm happy. If there's not much drink left I will take smaller sips to make the number even! I don't feel my life is run by this, however; it's just something I do.

It is important to recognise the difference between 'OCD' as a generalised slang term and the actual medical condition, which can be totally debilitating and consume every aspect of the sufferer's life. To help you understand and to enable you to distinguish between potentially non-OCD behaviour and true OCD behaviour, I have written some examples in the table overleaf.

Thought	Non-OCD behviour	OCD behaviour
'Have I locked the back door and turned off the cooker?'	Going back into the house to double-check once.	Potential fear: House being burgled, or house catching fire. Behaviour: Going back into the house to check again and again. Never being satisfied with what is found, or thinking the action was not performed right, or could have involved a mistake… Outcome: A significant part, or all of the person's day is taken up with constantly checking and re-checking.
'I should wash the kitchen surface as the cat has just been on it.' OR 'I should wash my hands after using the public toilet.'	Wiping down the kitchen with anti-bacterial spray once. OR Washing hands once, but just a little bit more thoroughly.	Potential fear: The person or a loved one will become ill. Behaviour: Endlessly thinking there are germs on the work surfaces (or airborne), and endlessly cleaning everything. OR Endlessly washing hands over and over to avoid what feels like an imminent threat of contamination. Outcome: Again, lots of time is wasted, and the person feels their hands are never quite clean enough, so to enable them to relax, they need to perform the actions again and again, possibly until their hands are red-raw and the skin is cracked.

'Will I listen to this CD again? Will I watch this DVD again? Do I need this ornament?'	Having a collection of CDs or DVDs, keeping some that the person might watch/listen to some day, or throwing away some they know they won't. Having a 'spring clean' and clearing out items they might not use anymore, and keeping some things that might be sentimental.	Potential fear: Something bad might happen if something is thrown away. Behaviour: Keeping things 'because they may be needed one day', to a ridiculous extreme. Outcome: The person's space is piled high with old and quite possibly useless items.
'What if I run someone over in my car today?'	Realising that most people have odd thoughts that pop into their heads from time to time, and that it is not really much of a big deal.	Potential fear: The person will act out the thought they are experiencing. Behaviour: The person may decide it is better if they do not leave the house and avoid certain places. They may feel that they are a terrible person for having these thoughts, creating elaborate rituals to neutralise them. Outcome: The person spends a lot of time in their own head, and consequently can lose friendships and become isolated.
(leaving the bathroom) 'The towels in the bathroom look a bit untidy.'	Popping back into the bathroom to fold and straighten them, so they look presentable for guests.	Potential fear: Something bad might happen to the person or a loved one if the towels are not straight. Behaviour: Going back into the bathroom repeatedly, as the towels never seem to look straight and tidy enough. Outcome: Most of the day is wasted arranging and re-arranging the towels.

As you can see from the above, a real threat and a perceived, and often irrational, threat are two very different things. However, people suffering from OCD, despite often identifying an irrational thought or an unrealistic threat as such, are unable to ignore it. Their perceptions of the level of danger, either to themselves or to others, usually loved ones, can cause their anxiety levels to rise, if they ignore it. This feeling can become so overpowering that they over-intensify their own sense of responsibility. Their anxiety spikes even further, pushing them into the hands of their compulsive behaviours in order to try to stop bad things from happening to them or others. The sufferer does not want these obsessional, intrusive thoughts in their head, so they can go to extreme lengths with their compulsions to try to repel them.

Aimee, an OCD sufferer, says:

> My OCD traits make me very rigid in my routines, and I am anxious to break them because I fear that it will prevent the 'perfect' outcome. I rationally know that the steps I am taking to ensure perfection are ridiculous and often detrimental to me, but a husk of belief keeps me repeating these habits over and over again. My mind focuses on the one time when my routines actually did serve me well and seems to let slide all the times they have had no impact whatsoever on the events to come – I am aware that this is a cognitive bias, but I just cannot stop!

There is so much information available now, we can often end up utterly baffled and vaguely hysterical, and therein lies the problem. The term 'obsessive compulsive disorder' actually covers a multitude of different behaviours; the condition can affect people in a multitude of different ways. To try to understand and gain more insight into the condition, many people may type 'OCD' into Google. The definition they find might be something like this:

> Uncontrollable, unwanted and repetitive OBSESSIVE thoughts that seem disgusting or frightening to you, and as a corollary to that, repetitive ritualised COMPULSIVE behaviours you feel you have to perform to neutralise these thoughts.

In layman's terms: 'The worst possible thoughts at the worst possible time.'

Natasha, explains what having OCD feels like to her:

> Having OCD is having a wheel constantly turning in my mind, that when I am having a tough day goes faster and faster and is unable to stop until I have physically spoken my thoughts aloud and taken their power away.

As OCD is often not visible to the outsider, it can also be hard to diagnose. The sufferer will no doubt, at some point, have thought that he/she was losing their mind, up until diagnosis; even then, for some, it can be difficult to come to terms with and accept what is happening to them. They will probably have known for some time that something is potentially not quite right, but their mind can trick them into thinking there is nothing wrong, so the diagnosis of a legitimate mental illness can sometimes come as a shock. However, for some sufferers, the OCD may have become such an ingrained part of their everyday life that they may not even really be aware there is an issue and formal diagnosis can therefore come as even more of a shock.

For someone suffering in silence it can take an act of great courage and strength to admit to a loved one, or a medical professional, that there may potentially be something wrong. Once it is all out in the open, it can be such a relief for them to know they are not losing their grip on reality and that what they are experiencing is a very common mental health issue suffered by millions of people across the globe.

My Samantha says of how she thought she was going crazy, and how relieved she was when she finally opened up to me:

Before I found the courage to tell my family about what was going on in my head, I felt extremely confused and ashamed, and most of all like I was going round the bend. I literally thought I was going crazy. I didn't know what it was or how to explain it; it probably took up 95 per cent of my brain and left me with just 5 per cent trying to hide it and pretend I was okay, but of course the high percentage taken up by the OCD soon showed its true colours. Thankfully, my mum knew that something was up, and when I got to the point where it was consuming everything, that's when my mum stepped in and encouraged me to explain EVERYTHING. What a relief it was to get it all out.

OCD is recognised by the professional medical community and can be treated successfully with time, perseverance, determination, the right therapy for the individual and, in some cases, medication. No two cases are ever the same – they are all unique to the individual sufferer – which is why treatment techniques and recovery journeys are so varied. Sadly, there is no magic pill, and whilst acceptance, understanding, support and patience are paramount to the sufferer's recovery, the only person who can really make the change is the sufferer. It is not an easy journey, but it is definitely one worth taking.

So what causes OCD?

There are two parts to the workings of OCD:

1. The first part is an involuntary, seemingly uncontrollable thought, image or urge ('intrusive thought') that repeatedly enters a person's mind, otherwise known as an 'obsession'. Such intrusions can cause high levels of anxiety, disgust and/or unease. A person experiencing intrusive thoughts will not invite them or enjoy having them, but cannot seem to stop them from occupying their mind. Some people describe these thoughts as being 'like

a stuck record', and just as irritating, yet actively trying to stop them can often make them worse. The thoughts can take up so much of a sufferer's mental space that, at times, they can find it difficult to concentrate for any length of time, so making their everyday life and routine a struggle.

2. Following on from the obsessive thoughts are the 'compulsions', which are a form of repetitive behaviour or mental acts that the sufferer feels they need to carry out to try to temporarily relieve the unpleasant feelings and anxiety brought on by the obsessive thoughts. These thoughts can make a person feel a seemingly uncontrollable desire to act out rituals and repetitive behaviours to make the intrusive thoughts safe, so taking their power away, or to make the sufferer feel temporarily at ease. The sad irony is that in most cases it only makes the obsessions worse, so perpetuating the problem.

In its simplest form, OCD occurs in a four-step pattern:

1. Obsession – the mind of the sufferer is overwhelmed with a constant obsessive fear or concern, such as their home catching fire.
2. Anxiety – the obsession provokes a feeling of intense anxiety and distress, often causing the 'worst case scenario' to be envisaged or imagined, sometimes repeatedly.
3. Compulsion – a pattern of compulsive behaviour is adopted in an attempt to reduce the anxiety and distress, such as checking all electrical and gas appliances many times before leaving the home or going to bed.
4. Temporary relief – compulsive behaviour brings momentary relief from anxiety.

After each cycle the thoughts will most likely return more strongly than before; therefore, more rituals will have to be performed to make the thoughts and feelings disappear (which may happen, but again only temporarily); then the thoughts come back more strongly, so the rituals will need to be performed again, and then the thoughts will come back again... creating a never-ending unhealthy cycle. Before the sufferer knows it, most or all of their time will be used up in this well-intentioned, but ultimately frustrating and futile, activity.

Janet explains her thoughts on her experience of OCD:

> Doing something you don't want to do before something you do want to do.

OCD symptoms can range from mild to severe. Some sufferers may spend an hour or so a day engaged in obsessive compulsive thinking and behaviour, but sadly for others the condition can completely take over and rule their lives. Whichever is the case, it is extremely frustrating and very destructive for the person having to carry out these rituals, as it is also for the people around them watching it happen.

It is not clear what causes OCD and, although there are various theories surrounding its development, it is currently thought to be a combination of biological, genetic, cognitive and environmental factors acting together or individually as a trigger.

Biological

Biological differences have been recognised in certain parts of the brain between OCD sufferers and non-sufferers, raising the possibility that certain people may be born with a biological predisposition, although findings remain inconclusive. Abnormalities or imbalances in the brain's neurotransmitters – including serotonin – have been highlighted, neurotransmitters being the chemicals the brain uses to transmit information from one brain cell to another. Normal levels of serotonin can lead to a natural state of contentment, but studies[1] have shown that people with OCD have an imbalance in these levels. However, the scientific community remains divided over whether low levels of serotonin cause OCD or OCD causes low serotonin levels. It is still unclear and research continues. It is a bit of a chicken-and-egg question.

Genetics

OCD can often seem to 'run in the family'. It is thought that almost half of all registered cases show a familial pattern. Research[2] shows that if someone has a close family member with a history of OCD, there could be a greater chance of developing the illness than someone with no family history. Genes are likely to play a role in the development of the condition, although they appear to be only partly responsible. It may be asked, however, why if one family member can learn OCD habits from another,, do individual family members have different symptoms of OCD? Researchers looking for genes that could be linked to OCD have still to find them, so the research remains inconclusive with regard to genetic inheritance.

Personality traits

People with certain personality traits may be more likely to develop OCD than others. An example would be someone who is a neat, meticulous, methodical person with high standards – a perfectionist perhaps.[3] OCD may also be a result of simply being more prone to becoming anxious, worried and tense, or having a very strong sense of responsibility for the self and/or others.

Dysfunctional beliefs

Some experts suggest that OCD could develop from dysfunctional beliefs and interpretations. The sufferer may believe that they have more responsibility over a situation than they actually do; because of this their reaction may be out of proportion. An example of this could be that while most people experience sudden and intrusive thoughts at some point, such as thinking that they might push someone in front of a car, most would dismiss this as a passing thought and not believe that they might actually act on it. However, the person with the dysfunctional beliefs might think that they could actually act upon the intrusive thought, which potentially could heighten their anxiety levels, prompting them to develop a compulsive behaviour to try to prevent it happening, and so the OCD cycle begins.

Infection

'Strep throat' in children has also been connected to OCD, not as the actual cause, but as a possible trigger for symptoms in children who are predisposed to the disorder as part of the body's natural response to the initial strep throat infection. This type of OCD is called 'paediatric autoimmune neuropsychiatric disorder associated with Streptococcus' (PANDAS).

Peggy looks back at what she thinks triggered her OCD:

It started when I reacted to a preschool booster for polio. I had hallucinations during the night. One of the monsters, Hawkeye-One-Eye, seemed to enter my head and tell me to do all these daft things, such as certain stairs could not be stepped on, imaginary friends had to be saluted!

Other mental health problems

From reading my own story in brief at the start of this book you may already know I have lived with and cared for my own daughter who has suffered from anorexia nervosa and OCD – hence I am writing from first-hand experience. In retrospect, I think Samantha had mild OCD tendencies when she was much younger, though, at the time, I put them down to her funny little habits and quirkiness of character rather than anything to be alarmed about. It was only after her challenges with anorexia nervosa had disappeared that I became aware that things were still not quite right with her, and on reflecting back over the years realised that the OCD had in fact always been there, waiting in the wings, ready to be unleashed.

Over time and through my experience as a mental health counsellor, I have come to believe that there are very strong links between eating disorders, particularly anorexia nervosa, and OCD. A significant number of my clients who are recovering / recovered from anorexia nervosa have displayed recognisable OCD traits and, although the relationship between the two conditions remains relatively unstudied, mental health specialists can sometimes mistake one condition for the other. The behaviours that result from both OCD and eating disorders can occasionally appear so similar that it proves very difficult to determine which of the two disorders the patient has, or if both are simultaneously present, and if so, which disorder is mainly responsible for bringing about the other. In cases of both anorexia nervosa and bulimia nervosa, obsessions with food and body image lead to levels of anxiety that can only be reduced by ritualistic compulsions, just as the OCD sufferer is compelled to check and double check if doors are locked. There has been speculation for decades about the parallels between the two conditions and the possibilities of one disorder appearing as another. Add to that the considerable percentage of eating disorder sufferers who also possess at least one other anxiety disorder, the majority being OCD. The connection between the two, in my opinion, can no longer be ignored.

Understanding the nature of OCD

If you are living with or caring for someone with OCD, I probably know just how you are feeling right now. You are providing as much physical and emotional support as you are able to, being as present as you can be, but whatever you do, the sufferer seems so far removed from you, so disconnected, that they might as well be standing on top of the Grand Canyon – they are that far out of your emotional reach. My daughter was exactly the same – we all wanted the answers to make it right for her inside her head, to make everything magically disappear. She had battled an eating disorder for years, only to then be consumed by OCD, so we were all grasping for anything at all that could help her.

For anyone closely connected to OCD, be it a sufferer, a carer or a loved-one, it can be a very lonely and isolating experience. If you are the sufferer I have the greatest compassion for you; I have seen and felt how tormenting it can be for both you and the people who love and support you. You will no doubt, at some point, feel that you are losing your mind, particularly if the people around you are fearful, or dismissive about your problem. Or, on the other hand, you may be too frightened or embarrassed to tell anyone, leaving you feeling utterly trapped and unsafe in your own head. Please remember, you are not alone; you are not 'mad' no matter what the contents of your thoughts are; you will not be judged by people who truly accept and understand or those who try to. These are symptoms of a treatable mental illness, not a reflection on you as a person. And best of all, by reading material like this, you are well on the way to taking steps in a much more positive direction and expanding your understanding and knowledge.

Ethan looks back:

I found it very hard to open up and speak to anyone about my OCD for about a year or so, I felt so alone and like I was going crazy. My thoughts were so vivid and so violent that I was afraid no one would understand and take me seriously. One day I couldn't take it anymore and spoke to my Dad. He was a little shocked at first, but now he is my biggest supporter. I wish I had found the courage to open up earlier.

Chapter 1

If you are a loved-one or the carer it can be not only frustrating and confusing but also very upsetting, and at times push your patience to the limit and beyond.

Ann, the mother and carer of an OCD sufferer, explains how she felt:

> I felt angry and very frustrated. Angry because it changed our lives and I couldn't do what I wanted without considering how it would affect my daughter. Frustrated because there was no way I could 'fix' her.

The sufferer can at times seem evasive and rude, but usually they are not meaning to appear in that way. it is all part of the illness – their head is full of so much chaos that it is a major undertaking keeping things together, let alone hold a half-decent conversation with anyone. Opportunities to communicate with an OCD sufferer about how they feel should be encouraged; the information you receive from them will prove vital in the recovery process. Do not apply logic; accept that their mind is a confused place and that, in talking, they are providing you with an important glimpse into its inner workings.

To try to give you a better understanding of why the sufferer's head might be full, take for example someone with a contamination obsession coupled with washing/cleaning compulsions. They are constantly distressed, believing that their body is dirty and contaminated and that no matter how many times they wash it, it is never enough (obsessive), so they continue washing again and again and again, repeatedly scrubbing with force until their skin is sore (compulsive). In doing so, their anxiety levels dip slightly but only temporarily, until they have to come in contact with objects once more, touching a door-handle, for instance, which they feel could be contaminated with germs. In the overloaded and irrational mind of the sufferer, the door-handle could potentially harbour what they perceive to be life-threatening germs, so they again scrub their already damaged skin excessively with a harmful and toxic substance, such as bleach. The sufferer may then consider the possibility of airborne germs that can get into the cracks in their scoured skin, and start the whole process over again. Whilst this loop is on replay, the sufferer does not have the head space to think about the consequences of their actions and question them, or about the physical damage they are inflicting upon their body; all they can think about is appeasing the obsessions, however long they last.

Envisage yourself facing that prospect every hour of every day, on a repetitive loop of thought, trying to neutralise with a recurring compulsive act, to rebalance the anxiety and feelings of inner unease. Imagine the mental trauma being inflicted on the sufferer as they try desperately to process these invasive thoughts day in, day out. How harrowing it must be for them. Non-OCD sufferers would see healthy caution as washing their hands after a visit to the bathroom or to cleanse them of surface dirt prior to preparing food; it is perfectly normal and expected to wash your hands once for such purposes – but not for someone suffering from OCD.

Olivia says of how OCD has affected her:

> I have had OCD on and off for many years – from what I can remember, since I was about 12. It seems to revolve mainly around personal cleanliness, but can be triggered by anything, sometimes things that aren't even connected. My way of trying to deal with these thoughts is by washing my hands, to wash the bad thoughts away. On a bad day I can wash my hands up to 100 times. As you can imagine, this can take up a lot of my time and can also make my skin really sore. With help and medication, I have developed some coping strategies which have given me a part of my life back... and my hands!

The answer to these obsessions and compulsions can lie in the correct form of therapy, support and understanding, with each programme directed at the individual sufferer and their precise type of OCD. Once the type of OCD has been identified (see

Chapter 2) and a specific programme of recovery implemented, the sufferer can be encouraged to recognise and challenge the difference between healthy caution and irrational fear, hopefully realising that their worst fears were grossly exaggerated and not in any way factual or true, and that they were in fact completely safe. Therapy can only ever be successful if the person suffering from OCD really wants to change and accept the help available to them. Their self-doubt and guilt-ridden heart will already be pricking away at their conscience and they may not like the prospect of a recovery programme. However, unless they start to embrace and engage with the help and support available to them with an open mind, their recovery could potentially be hindered. Once they believe there is hope, no-one can want recovery more than the sufferer themselves.

Below is a summary of the familiar 'facts' which are often quoted in relation to obsessive compulsive disorder. They are, as we will discover in the rest of the book, myths which can prevent carers from getting to grips with, and really being able to understand, the illness.

Myth 1: 'Everyone is a bit OCD'

Truth: As I mentioned on page 8, there are two parts to OCD:
  Obsessions: Intrusive thoughts, pictures or urges.
  Compulsions: These are the actions and behaviours in which sufferers might engage to help release the anxiety caused by the obsessions.

There is a distinct difference between compulsive inclinations and **obsessive**-compulsive behaviours, the most important word being 'obsessive'. If someone has OCD, their life will most likely be consumed with the obsessive thoughts and compulsions, which can interfere with work, school and/or their social life, leaving little time for anything else. OCD has certain criteria required to make a formal diagnosis. Those criteria differentiate a sufferer from someone who is, say, a bit more thorough than the norm about certain aspects of their life.

Myth 2: 'OCD is just about cleaning and hand-washing'

Truth: OCD manifests itself differently in different people. Yes, there are a proportion of OCD sufferers who have a fear of germs which can result in hand-washing or extreme cleaning compulsions. However, obsessions can fixate on almost anything, from fear of contamination and illness to worrying about harming others, preoccupation with numbers and patterns, fear of dying or fear of a loved one dying. And, in the same way, the compulsive behaviours that accompany them can also vary widely.

Myth 3: 'Sufferers of OCD do not understand their behaviours are irrational'

Truth: Most OCD sufferers *do* know that the relationship between their obsessions and compulsions is irrational and the compulsions can be potentially harmful to themselves and others around them. However, it is hard for them to know when their brain is 'lying' to them whilst they are experiencing strong urges to obey its irrational commands.

Myth 4: 'Stress causes OCD'

Truth: Whilst stress can exacerbate the symptoms in sufferers, OCD is a mental illness which can incite uncontrollable fears and anxiety which will most likely occur with or without stressful situations.

Myth 5: 'OCD is rare in children'

Truth: Childhood-onset OCD is quite common, occurring in approximately 1 per cent of all children. Furthermore, recent research[4] has indicated that approximately half of all adults with OCD experienced symptoms of the disorder during their childhood.

Myth 6: 'People with OCD worry about things non-sufferers do not'

Truth: Everybody experiences worrying thoughts about becoming ill or a loved one being harmed, or what would happen if...? How many times have you personally touched wood for good luck, or saluted a magpie? Whilst you may do this occasionally, with the thought passing on as soon as the action has finished, someone with OCD will get trapped in a cycle, believing they have not performed the action correctly and that they have failed to ward off bad things from happening.

Whilst most of us have the same worries as a sufferer, non-sufferers are less sensitive to them and, in comparison, can generally quite easily brush them aside.

Myth 7: 'OCD only affects certain people'

Truth: OCD can affect anyone regardless of gender, race, sexuality, or social background. It has no limits.

Myth 8: 'OCD is not treatable'

Truth: Many sufferers of OCD do not seek treatment because they are embarrassed, or they think there is nothing that can be done to help them. However, I cannot emphasise enough that recovery is possible provided the sufferer truly wants it and is prepared to put in the amount of effort and energy that is required to work at it and not give up when things become overwhelming and difficult. Within Chapter 4 (A guide to therapies – see page 53) I explore many different types of treatment, all of which have been successful in relieving the symptoms of OCD in some people and helping sufferers to move onto a positive recovery path.

Chapter 2

Types of OCD

Suffering from OCD is like having an unwelcome intruder in your head who arrives without warning or invitation, bringing along a big suitcase of psychological baggage. It noisily unpacks and becomes a selfish and unwanted squatter, and as time progresses it begins to wreak havoc, adding more and more baggage, until, in a short space of time the sufferer feels that their mental space is not their own anymore, because the OCD has built a powerful mountain of mental torment and chaos inside their head. It festers, unleashing its torture on the unsuspecting victim until they surrender to its voice of unreason. There is no evicting this squatter without the sufferer's determination, alongside the right kind of help and support, be it from a professional and/or a loved one(s). The sufferer is fighting an internal war, but with no clear resolution. This can be utterly exhausting, and the more tired the person who has the OCD becomes, the more space the head creates for the intruder to occupy. Being at war with any part of yourself can never bring peace, either for the sufferer or for their loved ones.

Researchers and clinicians propose that OCD can be divided into five different types, based on the nature of the symptoms experienced. Due to the complexity of the condition, OCD will usually 'attach itself' to something the sufferer cares about particularly, or to their weaknesses. For this reason, no two people experience OCD in exactly the same way. It can also be multi-faceted, with some of the OCD traits being interlinked – in other words, sufferers can experience more than one kind of OCD at any one time. The five main types are listed below, but it is important to remember that this is by no means an exhaustive list and there will always be types of OCD that express themselves differently and that are not included here. However, in the main, sufferers will be focused on one or more of the following:

1. Contamination (mental or physical) – sufferers are sometimes referred to as 'washers and cleaners'
2. Checking – sufferers are sometimes referred to as 'checkers'
3. Symmetry and orderliness – sufferers are sometimes referred to as 'organisers'
4. Intrusive thoughts or ruminations – sufferers are sometimes referred to as 'obsessors' or 'ruminators'
5. Hoarding – sufferers are sometimes referred to as 'hoarders'.

1. Fear of contamination

Physical contamination

The primary fear or obsession is that something is dirty or contaminated in some way that may cause harm, illness or even death to the sufferer or someone close to them. The compulsion is to clean and wash in an attempt to 'correct' this thought. As with all OCD sufferers, whatever they do, it is never enough and often is taken to the extreme.

I have listed below some common examples of behaviours and the possible thought processes behind them:

• The person opens doors with their sleeve, elbow, foot or anything else to avoid contact with their hands. (*What if there are germs on the handle?*)

- The person avoids shaking hands with you, or if they do, quickly runs to the bathroom to wash their hands. *(What if the other person is not clean?)*
- The person will do anything to avoid visiting a GP surgery or a hospital. *(What if I contract MRSA, or any other disease?)*
- The person spends unnecessary hours cleaning their house. *(What if I contaminate the family? What kind of person would that make me?)*
- The person avoids eating out in public places. *(What if they have poor hygiene and do not wash up properly?)*
- The person avoids being in a crowd such as a busy shopping centre or train station. *(What if I rub up against a person who has not washed properly?)* This can sometimes be mistaken for agoraphobia (fear of open spaces and crowds).
- The person spends hours excessively brushing their teeth. *(What if I get gum disease?)*

Of course, cleanliness and basic personal hygiene are important. It is normal to wash yourself, or clean something thoroughly once or maybe even twice, but if you have this form of OCD the cleaning or washing is often carried out multiple times, accompanied by rituals of excessive skin and body washing, especially of the hands, until the sufferer feels clean, temporarily, but will never be satisfied they are clean enough. The internal dialogue will most likely be: 'enough is never enough, just once more, just in case, just to make sure'. As with most types of OCD, because of the time consumed, there can be a knock-on effect to the sufferer's working life, school life, family life and relationships, while of course there is potential damage to the sufferer's hands or other body parts that are scrubbed or over-washed. Hours can be literally swallowed up by this ritual being played on a permanent loop inside the sufferer's head.

Some sufferers may find themselves avoiding certain places where a negative and challenging experience has been had, as the association between the place and the trigger is still active (e.g. a cinema toilet), but what the sufferer does not always realise is that avoiding certain places will only make things worse, not better, as this only feeds the OCD and gives it more power.

Judith tells us of her long-term struggles:

> Once the thoughts and fear enter my head, I find they completely take over and cloud my thinking. It seems to have gotten worse, and the fear transfers onto everything I touch, which means I have to clean pretty much the whole house at any one time on a bad day. On a good day, when I seem to be able to almost push the thoughts away, I can narrow the cleaning down to one room. It really impacts my everyday life, so much so that at the moment I am unable to hold a job down.

Mental contamination

As well as the above stereotypical image of OCD, there is a lesser known form that involves fear of *mental* contamination. This usually arises from psychological or physical violation, such as being humiliated, criticised or verbally abused, causing the sufferer a feeling of internal dirtiness. The main difference between mental and physical contamination obsessions is that the issue is internal for mental contamination, not external. However, the rituals can be the same, showering or cleaning to excess to 'wash it away' – that is, to get rid of the feelings of being unclean. Issues of poor self-esteem can also be strongly tied in here, which again only fuels the OCD, making it stronger and therefore harder to challenge.

2. Checking

The primary fear or obsession here is that something may be damaged, or someone may be offended, by something the sufferer has done or not done, said or not said. The compulsion is the need to check that everything is okay and that nothing bad will happen.

To help you understand a little more what this entails, here are some examples:

- The person may continually drive past their house for fear of it being on fire, flooded or burgled.
- The person may continually check that their house windows and car doors are locked, for fear of being burgled.
- The person may call, text and email as soon as they have left the house, to make sure their loved ones are okay, for fear that they have been hurt.
- The person may constantly seek reassurance that they have not offended someone in some way.
- The person may continually check their body and spend a lot of time researching symptoms online for fear of having a terrible illness.
- The person may read and re-read a book over and over for fear they have missed something important or did not mentally absorb the text.

Samaira, a nurse, explains her need to re-read her learning materials:

> I have had mild OCD for many years. Since I qualified as a nurse, it seems to have progressed into my working life. I feel that I have to keep reading and re-reading all my learning materials from my university degree. I am in constant fear that I will forget all that I have learnt, impacting my ability to perform my job properly. I am now seeking help for this and have got a little better.

Of course, if we have concerns about any of these things, it is perfectly normal and natural to check just once, or even twice, but someone who has OCD will check again and again, sometimes for hours on end, which of course can have a knock-on effect on their job, study, work, relationships and life in general. The checking can also damage the objects being checked, not to mention how it affects the quality of the sufferer's life.

Steve, an OCD sufferer, talks of his constant need to check:

> The avid fear of leaving the house unlocked means I have to check the locks at least three times. All the switches have to be checked too. It appears the longer I am leaving the house for, the longer it takes to lock up – that is, if I am going to the shops checking will take five minutes vs one hour if I am flying to the USA. This has led me to pull at least six door/car handles off in my OCD career.

3. Symmetry and orderliness

Most of us know a good handful of people who like to have things 'just so', or to be 'perfect', and we sometimes say they are 'so OCD'. Perhaps they are or perhaps they are not. The person who suffers from this form of OCD may have to arrange and rearrange objects until they are 'just right' over and over again; this is the compulsion. The obsessive fear is that perfect order is necessary to avoid uneasiness and distress, or to prevent harm occurring. This could range from lining up cushions perfectly, or having the cans in the kitchen cupboards with all the labels facing forward, or the perfect pile of towels in the bathroom with the toiletries placed in a specific way. These things in themselves are not an issue, unless their absence causes anxiety or discomfort to the person, and a form of OCD can then develop.

Jenny explains how everything has to be 'just so' for her:

> I need to see everything is uniform – for example, cups must have the handles all facing the same way, glasses must be put in cupboards in size and group order (ad hoc won't suit me at all!). Coloured plastic cups and plates must be in colour order (dark to light, unless there are light and dark green, say; they must stay together, then dark and light pink etc). Clothes must

be in colour order too – all black together and again reducing in colour order to white. All hangers MUST be the same.

Shoes must be in boxes (the same type of boxes, all clear plastic) and stacked in order of type (boots together, shoes together, sandals).

Bags should ideally have a matching purse but if one is not available then the next best alternative would be a brand or colour match.

Writing must be neat and uniform – if I'm writing a list it's either all in block capital letters or cursive, not a mixture of both. I can't stand messy writing.

If none of this happens I feel very uncomfortable and I could not sleep if I knew a white shirt was in with the black clothes – I would have to change it immediately.

The problem is exacerbated when the sufferer starts spending an inordinate amount of time getting things lined up 'just right' or in the 'right order', always ensuring everything is perfect before they leave the house or car – which could make them late for work, school, appointments or other timed commitments. As with other forms of OCD, the sufferer may avoid social contact within the home environment in the hope of preventing any symmetry and/or order being disrupted; this in turn can have a negative effect on both family and relationships in general, and in some cases can result in isolating the sufferer.

4. Ruminations and intrusive thoughts

Ruminations

'Ruminating' is a mental act whereby a person thinks carefully and intensely about a specific subject. The sufferer will go over and over something in their mind, without coming up with a suitable solution or answer that they are able to move on with. Often these ruminations are not harmful. The person may

endlessly ponder seemingly imponderable questions, such as:
- 'What is the meaning of life?'
- 'How did it all start?'
- 'What was there before it all started?'
- 'What happens after you die (…if anything)?'

Ruminators will play out many different situations and scenarios over and over again in their minds, rarely reaching a satisfactory conclusion; this can cause them to become profoundly distant and detached from reality. As the thoughts are continually repetitive and not voluntarily produced, they can cause the sufferer extreme distress.

Intrusive thoughts

Our imaginations know no limits and have no boundaries. Most people will experience intrusive thoughts of some kind, at some point in their lives; these can be centred around violence, blasphemy, sex or religion, to name just a few. These thoughts often, for most people, will come and go. However, for an OCD sufferer, these thoughts can be constant and do not leave the mind, so triggering debilitating anxiety. OCD sufferers will compulsively try to neutralise or invalidate these thoughts; however, the more they obsess, the stronger and more frequent the thoughts can become, so feeding into their biggest fears. This can lead to sufferers questioning themselves, and constantly seeking reassurance that they are not capable of acting on their thoughts. And so begins the never-ending cycle of obsessions and compulsions.

Natasha talks of her intrusive thoughts:

> The intrusive thoughts can come at random times and have lessened over tme as I have learnt not to allow them to have power over me. The key with intrusive thoughts is to take their power away as they are always about the stuff you are most scared of.

As you can probably imagine, intrusive thoughts can cover a vast array of subjects. Below, I have covered the more well-known and recognised OCD-related concerns within these seven sub-categories:

1. Religious
2. Magical thinking
3. Relationships
4. Sexual
5. Violent
6. Suicidal OCD
7. Pure O

Religious intrusive thoughts

OCD can tap into our most sensitive, weak and sacred areas, so people with deeply held religious beliefs can be prime contenders for these kinds of thoughts. This can also be referred to as 'scrupulosity'. Such thoughts can include:

- The person may believe that sins will not be forgiven by God and they will go to hell.
- The person may believe that they have left out certain prayers or not said them correctly.
- The person may have negative and/or disturbing thoughts about shouting blasphemous thoughts aloud within a religious setting.
- The person may believe that a bad power exists and will act on their thoughts to make bad things happen, or make good things happen to them in exchange for bad things happening to others, and they will be held responsible and that God will judge them for this.

The fallout from these distressing beliefs is that the sufferer will avoid religious activities and places of worship out of fear of their thoughts, distancing themselves from friends, family and fellow worshippers. Most will find it difficult to find inner peace from their religion – it will be a form of internal, mental and spiritual torment.

Magical thinking

Magical thinking is an illogical thought pattern characterised by the linking of unrelated actions or events. This can be based on the fear that simply thinking about something can increase the probability of it actually happening, sometimes referred to as 'thought/action fusion'. The sufferer can become extremely preoccupied with lucky and unlucky numbers, words, colours, sayings and/or superstitions, associating them with tragic or bad things that could happen.

On its own, magical thinking is not classed as a mental illness (many of us are superstitious, after all); however, it can be interrelated with some other mental health issues. OCD sufferers can engage in a type of magical thinking in which their obsessive thoughts can cause them to carry out compulsions in an effort to ward off the thoughts. People diagnosed with schizophrenia and delusional disorders may also experience bouts of magical thinking.

Magical thinking can be so vast and unique to the individual, depending on their own thought processes, that it is impossible to cover the full scope here, but below are some of the more common examples:

- The person may believe that if they do not carry on a chain letter or post on social media, something bad will happen to them or someone they care about.
- The person may believe that if they step on cracks in the pavement or walk over more than three drains at one time, something bad will happen.
- The person may believe that when the word 'death' is heard, the word 'life' has to be repeated to cancel it out, to prevent someone they know or themselves dying.
- The person may believe that if they think about an aeroplane being blown up, it is more likely to happen.

- The person may believe that certain colours or numbers have bad or good luck associated with them – for example, Friday the 13th.

Theo talks of his form of OCD, which has sadly taken over his life:

> I have just been diagnosed with severe OCD, which has completely engulfed my everyday thinking. It is centred around negative and positive thinking – for example, every time I hear or see something negative, like a bad word or an image, I feel compelled to balance it out with a positive word or image. I am unable to rest until I have corrected the negative thought; however, this can happen every minute of every day.

A non-sufferer of OCD will intellectually know that the thoughts and events listed above cannot possibly be linked, but in the mind of an OCD sufferer, they most certainly, unquestionably, are. They are convinced that their thoughts have very real power and are very dangerous, so leading them to have to perform many rituals in an effort to neutralise the thoughts – this can sometimes take hours. They will more than likely not be able to interact with anyone else during this time because they feel so trapped within their own mind-set and isolated in their own thoughts. As so much space in their mind is being used up by this, there is little time for much else. It is a bit like having too many windows open on your computer – their mind has reached system overload. The impact of this on their everyday life can be devastating as they struggle to try to think straight.

Intrusive thoughts about relationships

Everyone usually has doubts and worries about their relationships from time to time, which is normal. However, some people suffering from OCD can have never-ending doubts and indecisions; sadly, more often than not, they are unable to recognise that their OCD is trying to sabotage their relationship. These obsessional thoughts and doubts can either relate to their own sexuality, the suitability of their partner and/or the relationship overall. Here are some examples:

- The person may obsess over whether they love their partner, making endless pros and cons lists, but never coming to a conclusion.
- The person may begin to doubt their love towards their partner, believing that their relationship could fail.
- The person may not normally be the jealous type, but the OCD feeling will slowly creep into and take over their life, leading them to question their loved one's loyalty, love and fidelity. This can in turn lead to doubt and constant questioning, frustrating their partner, which tends to cause tension in the relationship; sufferers may take this as a sign that the relationship is failing or has already failed.
- The person, in a bid to make themselves feel better (at least temporarily), may constantly seek reassurance from friends, family or themselves, remembering and holding on to the past good times to help satisfy their doubts.
- The person may have strong feelings of guilt, constantly saying to themselves, 'Why am I feeling this way?' 'It is wrong to feel this way about my partner.' 'I am being pathetic.' However much they try, their doubts will dominate everything, making it difficult for them to decrease the compulsions and easier to be on their own, as opposed to in a relationship.

This way of thinking can place great strain on the sufferer's relationship, particularly if their partner does not understand OCD (which some, through no fault of their own, do not); the sufferer will eventually rid themselves of the relationship in a bid to stop the endless doubt and anxiety, if the partner has not already done so.

Becky says of how her obsessive thoughts have ruined her relationship:

> I was always doubting myself and my partner, was I good enough... was he good enough for me... was our relationship good enough. I became obsessed with the fact that I was not good enough and he was looking elsewhere. I was constantly checking his phone and social media, to try and gain validation. At the beginning, he did everything he could to reassure me that I was good enough, but towards the end I know I pushed him away.

However, it is quite possible to have a partner who is willing, despite the OCD, to be compassionate and understanding, and to be the sufferer's 'rock'. By helping and encouraging them as they challenge the thoughts, they are assisting the sufferer with their recovery. If the sufferer wants to get better, this can be a powerful combination.

Connor, an OCD sufferer, tells us of how supportive his wife has been throughout his recovery:

> My wife has been my saviour. She has supported me unreservedly throughout my OCD. When I was made redundant, my OCD got much worse; my wife noticed this and did lots of research and spoke to a few helplines to gain more information herself. She encouraged me to seek help, which was the first step forward in my recovery. I couldn't have got where I am today without her.

However, there can be instances, whereby, if two people in a relationship both have a susceptibility to mental illness, the consequences can be extremely destructive. Their mutual vulnerability can sometimes lead them to feed off each other's anxiety and fears, thereby exacerbating the mental illness for both of them.

Intrusive sexual thoughts

It is important to say here that sexual fantasies are quite normal, and the vast majority of us have had them at some point. It would only fall under the umbrella of OCD if a person felt there was something wrong with these fantasies, and feared acting them out in an unsuitable way. As with all types of intrusive thoughts, there is also a wide range of sexual obsessions; these could be with sexual identity or sexual thoughts about children or friends, incest, infidelity, violent sexual behaviour, or blasphemous thoughts combining religion and sex. Some of these obsessional thoughts may include the following. The person may fear that they:

- are attracted to a family member;
- will become attracted to a child, or have inappropriate thoughts about touching the child;
- may become attracted to someone of the same sex. Or if the person is gay, may become attracted to someone of the opposite sex;
- will have intrusive sexual thoughts about God or any other religious symbol.

Many people with OCD worry that the content of their sexual obsessions may indicate that they could be a rapist or paedophile or sexually perverted in some shape or form. It is important to say here that the sufferer experiencing these thoughts does not want to have them; they find them very upsetting, painful and guilt-provoking, and have no intention of acting upon them.

The knock-on effect of this type of OCD is that the sufferer may avoid public places in an attempt to avoid coming into contact with people, including children. It can be particularly difficult for a parent with this type of OCD, as it could cause them to avoid any close contact with their own children, leading to potential emotional distress for all involved. This allows the thoughts to not only win but to destroy the day-to-day life of the sufferer and the people who love them.

A sufferer may be very reluctant to open up and seek treatment because of the fear that they might be judged, labelled and/or misunderstood. However, it is important to remember that a trained professional would immediately realise this is no more than OCD, and the chance of the person acting on these thoughts, as with other types of OCD, is less than minimal.

Intrusive violent thoughts

Violent thoughts may involve both mental pictures and urges. These thoughts can include, for example, those in which the sufferer may see themselves beating, stabbing, throttling, actually killing or otherwise injuring their loved ones, themselves or even the neighbour's cat. These thoughts can be highly unpleasant and painful to the sufferer, especially because, in most cases, people suffering from this type of OCD are no more likely to act upon the thoughts and urges than someone not suffering.

The sufferer may have thoughts about:

- hurting a child, pet or loved one
- unintentionally touching someone with the ultimate aim of harming them
- using a penknife or razorblade with the intention of harming someone
- poisoning the food of animals and/or loved ones
- pushing someone off a bridge or cutting someone
- and then acting on those thoughts.

Having this type of OCD can not only be distressing but also extremely isolating, with the knock-on effect being, sadly, that the sufferer will go to great lengths to avoid public places or social events to ensure they do not come into close contact with anyone who could potentially trigger these thoughts. They may even go to the extent of locking away knives and razorblades, refusing to cook for the family, refusing to drive (in case they think about deliberately driving into something) and/or engaging in seemingly extreme avoidance behaviours.

In most cases, people suffering from this kind of OCD have convinced themselves that they are a bad or nasty person, just for having these types of thoughts. To sufferers and their carers, these thoughts can seem shocking. Due to the sheer graphic nature these thoughts often have, endlessly analysing them can be upsetting, and of course there is the fear of being misunderstood, judged or labelled by people; sufferers can therefore be reluctant to seek treatment or share the problem with anyone.

5. Hoarding

Hoarding is basically the inability to rid oneself of seemingly unusable, damaged and/or worn-out possessions. Many people can be loosely labelled as 'hoarders'; however, for those who suffer from this complex form of OCD, it can be a very stressful and quite extreme illness, leaving the person physically and emotionally drained, with, in some severe cases, impairment to the sufferer's day-to-day living.

There are three specific types of hoarding:

- **'Prevention of harm' hoarding** – A sufferer will fear harm will be caused if they throw things away. For example, a sharp object if discarded in the trash could somehow seriously harm anyone who comes into contact with the disposal of rubbish.
- **'Deprivation' hoarding** – A sufferer feels they will find a need for something later in life so does not know whether or not they should throw it away. Sometimes this is a reflection of previous deprivation in their lives.
- **'Emotional' hoarding** – In the UK there was a TV soap opera that covered this in a storyline. A husband passed away and the wife could not throw anything out for deeply sentimental reasons. She felt it was her last remaining

connection to him. It is as I have described above, a mental attachment to meaningful objects that is natural and in some ways, beautiful, but not realistic or desirable when taken to an extreme, or if there is an underlying belief that life can never be good again, so it is best to cling on to the past.

Hoarding in general may spring from the fear that nothing new or better is coming, so it would be best to hold on to what the person has, or it could even be a mental attachment to meaningful times in the past associated with those items.

Lorna talks about her struggles with OCD and hoarding:

> My need to keep things got so out of control that it caused my partner to leave, as he could not handle the hoarding anymore, as it took over our flat. My mind tells me that I will not be able to live my life properly without these items, but I know deep down inside that it is has taken my life instead.

Other types of OCD

Suicidal obsessions and S-OCD (suicidal obsessive compulsive disorder)

Suicidal obsessions are a specific type of suicidal thought that is unique to the individual with this type of OCD. A person suffering from S-OCD has an inner dialogue which is often different from their intentions and beliefs. They will frequently experience disturbing and uncomfortable suicidal obsessions that they know they have no intention of carrying out but are unable to stop intruding. For most, they do not want to actually carry out the fatal act but are consumed with the thoughts of it, in complete contradiction to their actual state of mind. For example:

- 'What if I swerve into oncoming traffic?'
- 'What if I jump onto those train tracks in front of that train?'

- 'What if the impulse urges me to jump off a building?'
- 'What if I'm harming myself somehow without knowing it?'
- 'What if I cannot stop myself from driving off a bridge?'

The sufferer, most of the time, has no intention of committing suicide yet can become completely tormented and frightened that they could unintentionally bring about their own death as a consequence of their obsessional thoughts. They will often turn to rituals to neutralise these obsessions and thereby temporarily lower their anxiety levels. Examples of such rituals include:

- checking that there are no lethal items in the house
- checking their own written conversations (notes, texts, social media) to make sure there is no suicidal intent
- avoiding others who make them feel negatively about themselves or trigger negative memories
- seeking reassurance and validation from others that they would never harm themselves, and are not displaying the signs of someone who has that intention
- ruminating about the reasons why they would never kill themselves and that they are actually opposed to suicide.

These and other behaviours that the sufferer creates will feed the OCD and in turn intensify the problem, which we already know will fuel and drive the never-ending and dangerous cycle that the person's OCD is controlling.

It is paramount to say here that, although the sufferer, most of the time, does not want to carry out these acts, any form of suicidal thoughts should be taken seriously, and professional help should be sought *immediately*.

'Pure O'

'Pure O' means 'purely obsessional'. This phrase can occasionally be used to describe a type of OCD, where the sufferer may experience upsetting and painful intrusive thoughts with no outward sign of compulsions (so no cleaning, checking, etc). Instead, the compulsions take place within the person's mind. The term 'pure O' can therefore be slightly misleading, as it suggests there are no compulsions at all. As they are just not as noticeable as physical compulsions, this makes it difficult to define what these compulsions are.

Some examples may include the person:

- constantly repeating numbers or phrases in their head
- continually checking how they feel (for example, checking to see if they still love their child)
- continuing to check how they feel about a thought (for example, checking if they are still 'appropriately disgusted' by a thought).

The three main components of OCD

Irrespective of the type of OCD that a person may be suffering from, there will be many unique features to each condition. However, the following three components will more than likely be present:

1. **Triggers** – Obsessions may be triggered by objects, circumstances, smells or something seen or heard on television, social media, the internet or in a discussion. Obsessive fears usually move beyond a specific trigger; they can transfer onto anything that might look like the trigger or have been near it. For example, if the trigger is a bar of chocolate, this could transfer onto the fridge shelf it was sitting on, and then the fridge itself, the kitchen the fridge is in, the house it was in and then the supermarket it was bought from, and so on.

2. **Avoidance** – Due to the above triggers, sufferers might find themselves avoiding certain objects, situations,

people and places. Most OCD sufferers will find it easier to completely avoid situations that trigger the thoughts and compulsions. For example, a sufferer who has urges to avoid all the cracks in pavements and roads may find it easier just not to leave the house rather than go through the tiring, repetitive, continuous compulsions and mental torment.

3. **Reassurance** – The sufferer will constantly seek reassurance from trusted people, but no matter how much those people give, it will never be enough. For every compelling argument carers offer, they are normally frustratingly met with a 'Yeah, but what if...' from the sufferer, and sufferers can be very creative about such negative possiblities.

A lot of sufferers with OCD may twist the truth; it is paradoxical really that the sufferer seeks reassurance that all is going to be okay, yet at the same time looks for and creates reasons why it will not be! We have to bear in mind that the sufferer's way of thinking is not always rational. They will find it easier, in the short term, to give in to the demands of the OCD, rather than to challenge it.

As my Samantha dittos below:

Looking back, when the OCD was at its worst, I suppose it was easier to give in to the thoughts, temporarily pleasing it. Although you know deep down there will be a next time, and a next time, and a next time...

Once I found the courage to say no to the OCD, I began to realise long-term that the more I defied the OCD the weaker it got, and the easier it was to beat it.

Let me end this chapter with the thought, IT CAN BE DONE. Most people suffering from OCD will have people around them who can and most likely will support them. What is crucial, however, above all else, is that the sufferer really wants to recover… it HAS to be driven by them, remembering always that recovery is both achievable and sustainable.

Chapter 3

Recognising OCD and seeking treatment

Having an understanding of how the OCD mind works, and being knowledgeable on the subject, are probably the two most powerful tools you, as the carer, can have when confronting a loved one or a friend who you think may be suffering from OCD. Even though it is a relatively common illness, OCD is still woefully misunderstood and, sadly, at times, not taken seriously. Due to the complexity of the illness it also can often be misdiagnosed, as some of the symptoms presented can often mirror traits from other mental illnesses.

The bridge between being ill and seeking and receiving treatment in OCD sufferers is a precarious one to navigate, not only for sufferers themselves, but also for the people surrounding them. Leading up to and after diagnosis, many parents, partners or carers of OCD sufferers can make themselves ill by worrying, blaming themselves, raking over the past with a fine-toothed comb and frantically trying to pin-point where they went wrong. Sleepless nights, high levels of stress and even depression can ensue. This is totally counterproductive, because the feelings of guilt can run two ways – OCD sufferers tend to have a hugely over-developed sense of guilt, which can be magnified when they see the effect their illness is having on their loved ones and friends. Their solution to these feelings of shame is usually to bury themselves further in their illness, and so the situation can become a vicious circle.

Janice, a carer and mum, looks back on the guilt she felt:

> Looking back, I wasted many hours blaming myself for my son's diagnosis of OCD. I continually blamed myself and questioned if it was all my fault. In hindsight, now my son is in recovery, I realise that blaming myself was a total waste of my time and energy, at a point where it could have been put to better use.

It is also important for parents, partners and carers to be well enough to support the process of recovery. It is essential for all concerned that carers try to maintain their own physical and emotional wellbeing during this very difficult time. Whether the sufferer is young and still living at home, or older, the people around them will be of the utmost importance in supporting and guiding them towards health and recovery.

Unfortunately, there is no quick and easy laboratory test that can give an immediate diagnosis. Focusing on the physical symptoms alone can lead to maybe missing the emotional signs. Knowing this is the parent's/carer's biggest ally, as OCD can often be extremely difficult to identify in the early stages. However, there are certain patterns and tendencies that may help you to determine that something could be amiss. In my personal experience, a dramatic change in personality and behaviour can be one of the biggest warning signs. Whether your loved one is usually eccentric and quirky or insular and private, you may know them well enough to be able to recognise the differences over and above their usual mannerisms.

To give you more of an idea, below are some of the emotional and behavioural changes that may be present in someone with OCD. The person may:

- become very anxious, irritable and emotional
- have a continual low mood and find it hard to shake it off
- be continually worrying about anything and everything

- be continually tense, uptight and/or moody
- feel that nothing is ever 'right – whatever they do, it is never enough
- become very distant, preoccupied and uncommunicative
- develop very low or non-existent self-esteem and self-worth
- talk to themself or mutter under their breath more than usual
- start blinking heavily and awkwardly, as if they are trying to blink bad thoughts away.

It is important to say here that just because someone is showing some or all of these symptoms it does not necessarily mean they have OCD. I would advise you as a loved-one or caregiver to use your own intuition to guide you in identifying whether these symptoms are typical of the person you know or are somewhat out of character for them.

Once your attention has been drawn to some of the initial personality changes, you may gradually start to notice other behaviours beginning to emerge – for example, in the way the person speaks or acts. As OCD is an illness of the mind, and cannot always be seen, the person's intrusive thoughts and internal obsessions may be more difficult to detect initially, so, once again, their behaviour and overall demeanour can play a crucial part in early intervention.

Some physical signs and behaviours you might start to notice include the person starting to:

- constantly check things, whether it be door locks, ovens, car doors, taps, electrical appliances, or… the list goes on
- constantly count, whether out loud or muttering to themselves under their breath
- repeatedly clean their hands, or other parts of their body, or certain objects
- line up and organise objects – for example, arranging items to face a certain way, or clothes in certain colour orders

- say or repeat prayers or mantras to cancel out their obsessive thoughts.

It is worth remembering that as much as these compulsions can bring anxiety for the sufferer, so too can the prospect of giving them up. They may see all their thoughts and behaviours as preventing something bad from happening; some sufferers even visualise their OCD as a loyal friend who is guarding their back, rather than a bully who creates an endless, repetitive, destructive pattern.

Chris tells us of how his boyfriend's OCD became apparent when they moved in together:

> When we were first dating I noticed quite quickly that he was not a great time keeper; he would always be about 20-30 minutes late for arrangements, always seeming rushed and a bit flustered. After moving into our flat together, I realised why he was always late. I started to notice that he would spend a long time in the bathroom everyday cleaning himself and the room multiple times. This then started happening in the kitchen and slowly seemed to progress to the whole flat. It really started to affect our relationship. After speaking to him about it, he opened up a bit as to the reasons why he was doing what he was doing, and we are now thankfully on a path to seeking help.

In most cases, sufferers are aware that their thought processes, followed by their need to carry out rituals, are illogical, but they still feel compelled to carry out the demands of the OCD voice inside their head. For the carer, this is one of the most frustrating and difficult parts of their loved one's OCD to understand.

Aimee, an OCD sufferer, says of her OCD's need for approval:

> My mum literally pleads with me not to fry myself in the sun, but I feel that a tan makes me more attractive to others. My short-term need for approval and fear of being deemed ugly far outweigh the long-term threat of skin cancer!

Aimee's mum has no option other than to watch her daughter roast in the sun all day, unprotected, and fears for her health in more ways than one.

The person suffering may well be uncharacteristically cunning, creating distractions to mask the symptoms and their excessive behaviours – anything to avoid facing the reality of the situation. They may go to extreme lengths to cover up the fact that anything is wrong, but this does not mean that they are intentionally being deceitful, calculating or dishonest; it is all part of their illness, challenging their usually rational thoughts. They will often make excuses too for their unusual behaviour, saying: 'This is just the way I am' or 'I don't like germs, so I wash my hands because I may become ill if I don't.' Often, when the sufferer is caught up in the OCD thoughts and compulsions, they can be so entrenched in the 'moment' and the need to appease the demands of it, they are generally not able to think about the consequences that their actions will bring. For example, someone who has OCD about cleanliness and contamination, and uses hand washing with detergents as their release, probably will not think about the damage they are doing to their skin whilst they are carrying this behaviour out. Another example could be someone, again with OCD about cleanliness and contamination, but who uses cleaning surfaces and objects as their release, may not think twice about taking cleaning products from work, other people's houses or public places, if they are unable to source them themselves; the consequence will be the effect on other people and what they think of the sufferer.

The first and most important step towards OCD recovery is, the sufferer must want to get better him/herself. As soul-destroying as it is, attempts to rehabilitate sufferers who are not yet ready to acknowledge and deal with the problem are likely to prove fruitless. (However, with the assistance of the right kind of therapy and positive environment, a sufferer can be stabilised, so that their condition does not worsen. Getting actively better is what requires the sufferer to engage totally with treatment and the recovery process.)

For many parents, carers and friends, the reality of this is that they will probably have to play a waiting game. There are few things more exasperating than watching someone we care about suffer and being unable to intervene. So, what can be done in the meantime? Again, in this instance, knowledge is power. There are many treatments available, and it is important to understand what they entail and how they work. In this way, when sufferers express a desire to get better, their family and friends can leap into action and find the most appropriate source of help as quickly as possible.

To assist with this, there is an unbiased guide to some of the available treatments in Chapter 4. The speed with which you, as a parent or carer, can act at this point in time is also of paramount importance. Often the sufferer's OCD has peaks and troughs and they may yearn for recovery during the troughs, when they are at their worst, so it is important to get them into a positive and suitable environment while they are in the correct frame of mind and before any seeds of self-doubt can be sown by their OCD and begin to fester and grow. Remember, they have to really want to embrace this recovery thought process, to engage with any form of treatment.

Lucy talks of her realisation that she wanted to recover:

> I think I only realised I needed to recover after I started seeing life a bit more. Due to being in a disordered state and under depression I couldn't see life clearly or well so had no reason to recover. But after seeing my friends more and coming out of my shell again I began to see why I couldn't keep living life in my own shell.

Sue, Lucy's mother, says of their continuing journey:

> With support, challenging Lucy's OCD behaviours and getting
> her to question her own actions, has started to lead to a
> break-through. She is starting to see how 'abnormal' some of
> her habits were and make her own goals to change them. This
> is lifting the OCD need for total control in her head and she is
> starting to see more clearly what are 'normal' behaviours. We
> still have to complete our journey, but Lucy and ourselves now
> have renewed hope for the future.

After recognising that there is a problem, whether it be
the sufferer him/herself reaching out for help or a loved one
encouraging them, the first port of call should be your local
general practitioner (GP). At this stage, please remember that
no-one's time is ever wasted investigating the possibility of
OCD, even if the diagnosis turns out to be something different,
but the earlier the condition is identified, the earlier intervention
can take place, with the hope of a quicker and more effective
recovery for the sufferer and their family.

Recognising she needed urgent help, Natasha, took herself to
her local hospital:

> The day I recognised something was very wrong was the day I
> took myself secretly to the psychiatric unit at the hospital and
> said, 'Help me.' I knew what I was experiencing was not normal
> and thought I was going crazy.'

Actively seeking help can be a vital first-step forward towards
recovery. However, it is important to remember that GPs are not
miracle workers or mind readers, nor are they mental health
specialists, and whilst some may have substantial knowledge
and a special interest in OCD and other mental health issues,
some may not. Sadly, the very limited time slot they are allocated
for each patient can sometimes be insufficient to assess all of
their patients thoroughly. In a sector ruled by guidelines and

under constant scrutiny, time is one thing most GPs are sadly unable to offer.

Ahead of the appointment with the GP, it may be helpful if the sufferer makes a list highlighting their symptoms and how they feel they have changed over time. Having done so may help them at the surgery if they become anxious and forget the crucial facts. A diagnosis is only as reliable as the information the patient provides, so keeping the lines of communication as open as possible with the GP will assist greatly in the diagnosis and moving forward, not only in the initial appointment but in the long term. It might also be extremely helpful to arrange for someone to accompany the sufferer to their appointment; having an advocate present is beneficial to both parties (the sufferer and the GP) and can help the sufferer understand and remember the information given to them by the GP, whilst feeling reassured that they are being supported and listened to.

It is very important, at this stage, to encourage the sufferer to be as open and honest as they can be with their GP in the time frame they have, however frightening, uncomfortable and complicated the consultation may feel. The GP will make an initial assessment based on the information they have been given and hopefully offer both support and the relevant treatment route for their patient.

Expectations of GPs can be unfairly high and unfortunately not all appointments will conclude the way the patient or carer would like, so if this turns out to be the case, it would be prudent to make a fresh appointment straight away either to see another GP in the practice or to consider alternative treatments in the private healthcare system. However, sadly, even after initial formal diagnosis and referral for specialist help, the waiting lists for mental health treatments can be very long and in some circumstances, taking into account the psychology behind the illness, be unsafe for the sufferer depending on how embedded the OCD has become.

Julie talks of her family's frustration when trying to access help:

When my daughter was 16, we noticed her behaviour change quite dramatically over a period of around eight to 10 months. She was becoming very withdrawn and seemed to be avoiding seeing friends and social situations and not wanting to go to college. My husband and I started to get very concerned and so we arranged a doctor's appointment. The doctor was extremely helpful and put us on a waiting list to see a specialist on the NHS. Unfortunately, we had to wait four months for the initial assessment, at which she was diagnosed with OCD. We were given four weekly sessions of CBT, which was beginning to make a small difference. However, during this time, my daughter turned 18, which meant she had to be transferred to an adult service after those four sessions; three months on, we are still waiting for an appointment. We have no choice but to now look into private therapy, but this will be a very big financial strain on us.

There is no right or wrong way at this juncture, but weighing up the advantages and disadvantages of joining an NHS waiting list as opposed to seeking private alternative help should be carefully thought through. Private treatment costs money and this may prove a stumbling block for some, so my advice to parents, loved ones and caregivers would be to read and research as much as you possibly can about the diagnosis yourself. Knowledge is power and will help you make the right choices going forward, with and for the sufferer.

When our daughter, Samantha, was first diagnosed our GP was very supportive, always taking time to listen, understand and advise us to the best of his knowledge. Anything he was not too sure about he would look into after our appointment and report back to us, keen to work with us in the best interests of Samantha and us as a family unit. When he retired we thought that we would be right back to square one with a new doctor who might have little or no knowledge of OCD and anorexia nervosa, but we needn't have worried as we were blessed with yet another wonderful GP; she has been extremely helpful, so it is important to remember that there are many GPs out there who will, hopefully, be just as understanding and supportive.

Every sufferer's path to recovery is different, as are their individual experiences of the NHS, private healthcare and any alternative medical professionals they encounter; each person is individual and responds differently. If one treatment proves ineffective, it absolutely does not mean that the patient is 'incurable'; it simply means that the treatment is not working for that individual, so it is time to look for another; try different avenues until you find someone or something more suitable for the person suffering.

Brian says of his treatment journey:

> After struggling with OCD for many years, and realising that it was really affecting my life and wanting to do something about it, I tried three different types of therapy before I found the right one for me. I am now making good progress.

If possible, however difficult things get, try not to allow the sufferer to fall at the first hurdle. It is important to all try to move forward together, making a joint effort to find the right path that works for everyone. There will be ups and downs along the way and there can very much be a 'one step forwards, two steps back' scenario for a while; it can be a long road, but acceptance, understanding and perseverance are key. The sufferer needs all the encouragement you can give them to keep going until they get the help they need and deserve, so patience and open-mindedness are of the upmost importance. Propping the sufferer up for a little while is okay too, but they have to be able to walk alone at some point and take ownership of their road to recovery. For the process to flourish and be a success, they really need to want it 100 per cent for themselves. Being afraid of the unknown is a perfectly normal reaction when faced with the challenge of tackling a loved one and their mental illness. Please try not to feel daunted by the prospect of what lies ahead. Have courage, be strong and stand side by side with the sufferer, standing up to the testing times that are to come by communicating and uniting to confront it head on.

My Charlotte ends this chapter with:

> Having been around mental illness for 12 or so years, and from now working with Mum, I have seen how mental illness impacts the lives of everyone around it; not just the sufferer, but also family and friends. One of the most important things I have learnt is to talk – if you think something is wrong with a family member, friend or loved one, always talk with someone you trust, try not to brush things under the carpet, and be as open and honest as you can be.

Always remember: recovery is possible.

Chapter 4

A guide to therapies

As discussed earlier in this book, each form of OCD manifests itself in a different and unique way, because each sufferer is different and unique. In the same way there is no 'ultimate' treatment. For example, one OCD sufferer may respond very well to a certain treatment, while it may have little or no effect on someone else who has also been diagnosed with OCD. For some, a combination of therapies can be the answer. Whatever the details, it is essential that the sufferer and their carers choose a course of therapy which fuels and strengthens their desire to recover, as opposed to drowning and eventually killing that desire.

In order to be proactive during this frustrating time, one step which carers, parents and friends of sufferers can take is to arm themselves with a thorough knowledge of the various treatment options available. This chapter provides an unbiased guide to many of the different therapies available, both within the NHS and outside it. I have asked specialists within each field, all of whom I know personally, to explain a bit more about their therapy, to help you understand how their individual discipline can assist in combating OCD.

(You may notice some approaches overlap with others or combine elements from one with another – this is all part of the wide variation in what works for different individuals.)

Cognitive behavioural therapy (CBT)

CBT is one of the most well-known forms of therapy for treating someone suffering from OCD. The aim of CBT is to allow patients to tackle damaging patterns in their thought processes and reasoning, using discussion-based therapy, and by managing their behaviour.

I asked Liz Lisac, a professional counsellor/psychotherapist, to describe CBT. Liz says:

CBT is a talking therapy that focuses on how our thoughts and beliefs, and the way we think about situations, influence our feelings and consequently the way we behave.

It combines cognitive therapy (examining the things a client thinks) with behaviour therapy (examining the things a client might do).

It aims to help patients manage their problems by showing them how to challenge their thinking. For example, someone who feels fearful of social situations might start to avoid those situations even more. This avoidant behaviour then reinforces the original thought that social situations are fearful and should be avoided, creating a vicious cycle. A CBT therapist creates a structured framework in the session that aims to break this negative cycle of anxious thoughts, feelings and subsequent behaviours by working with the client to identify and challenge their negative thoughts and resulting anxious behaviours. Together therapist and client will collaborate to break the problem down into smaller parts. As these negative patterns are gradually challenged the therapist supports the client to try out new, less restrictive behaviours with the aim of improving the way the client feels.

CBT is most usually used to treat anxiety, OCD and depression but can also be effective with other mental health problems.

Liz explains how CBT works to treat OCD:

Obsessive compulsive disorder (OCD) is a mental health condition whereby obsessive thoughts and compulsive behaviours are experienced. The client might suffer from intrusive thoughts that provoke anxiety and then attempt to block the thoughts and anxiety with compulsive behaviour.

These compulsions then become rituals and the client finds themselves caught in a negative cycle. Someone with a fear of germs might find themselves continually handwashing and then actively avoid what might be a trigger situation, such as using a public toilet when travelling on public transport, where they fear germs.

CBT aims to help sufferers look at their fears and obsessive thoughts. Together the therapist and sufferer work to understand how the compulsion the sufferer has been using to stop the difficult feelings and thoughts has actually been making the situation worse and making the thoughts and feelings worse.

The recovery process can sometimes be more effective when one form of therapy works alongside other therapies that complement it. CBT can do just that. Liz said:

CBT can work well alongside complementary therapies that offer emotional and physical support. Since the body and mind are interrelated, it follows that if we are working on the mind and our thinking we will also notice how breathing, the way we hold our bodies and eating habits can affect anxiety levels, depression and OCD.

Mindfulness [see page 93] can also be very helpful, supporting the client to manage their anxiety as they are collaborating with their CBT therapist to change negative thinking patterns.

Nutritional therapy [see page 90], yoga [see page 91] and massage [see page 98] are all beneficial and can support a client who is working with a CBT therapist to manage anxiety/ depression and OCD.

CBT can be effective in the early stages of an eating disorder, but if an eating disorder is not treated early enough, once the body goes into starvation mode, thinking becomes more irrational and a patient might not be able to work collaboratively at a cognitive level.

Sometimes psychiatric support and a pharmaceutical therapy [see page 77] are needed alongside any CBT work if a client is experiencing chronic anxiety and depression or OCD.

This brings us onto 'exposure and response prevention', a form of cognitive behavioural therapy.

Exposure and response prevention (ERP)

Simply put, ERP is 'facing the things you fear'. It can be quite a distressing therapy for the sufferer to experience, but it is recognised as one of the most effective therapies in treating OCD. ERP is a form of cognitive behavioural therapy (CBT), and the most common form used to treat OCD. The principal aim of this method is to enable the person to become their own therapist and to provide them with the knowledge and tools to continue working towards their recovery. In short, ERP involves the sufferer with OCD facing their fears and then refraining from ritualising. During the therapy, the sufferer and therapist explore alternative ways to respond to the obsessional thoughts or doubts.

These exposure exercises often include doing things that could make the sufferer feel deeply uncomfortable and highly challenged. For example, a sufferer with obsessions related to contamination and cleanliness, might have to touch a dirty surface and wait for two hours before washing, having to learn to deal with the resulting high levels of anxiety without exercising their handwashing behaviours.

By directly facing their fears, the sufferer slowly begins to learn that the rituals and compulsions do not need to be carried out, and that they are safe and unharmed without doing so.

In many cases, CBT alone is highly effective in treating OCD, but for some individuals a combination of CBT and medication is needed to help reduce the anxiety enough for a person to start, and eventually succeed, in therapy.

Poppy, says of her experience of CBT and ERP treatment:

> Although, at times, it pushed me to my limits and beyond, making my anxiety sometimes unbearable, with time and perseverance, it has helped me to manage the OCD a lot better.

Dialectical behaviour therapy (DBT)

DBT has its origins in CBT and is similar in many ways. However, it differs in that it focuses on mindfulness, acceptance, validation and building trust. It was originally intended for people who had been diagnosed with 'borderline personality disorder', but has since been looked at for people with a range of mental health issues.

DBT is used exclusively with treating obstructive and dangerous patterns of behaviour. It does not search for or attempt to address the emotional origins of the OCD. It is therefore only usually recommended for a specific type of patient for whom delving into their past to explore their emotions might prove counterproductive.

Some examples of how the skills learnt from DBT can help with OCD might be:

- Learning to tolerate stress, either by self-soothing or by use of distraction
- Regulating emotions, by learning how to manage the anxiety surrounding the OCD; this should in turn help the sufferer to begin to notice a reduction in the need to carry out compulsions
- Using the skill of mindfulness (see page 93) to enable the sufferer to be more present in the moment, not hanging onto distressing thoughts and encouraging the sufferer to redirect them.

This therapy does not directly address the obsessions and compulsions, but rather gives the sufferer skills to enable them to cope with the anxiety associated with them.

Neuro-linguistic programming (NLP)

NLP was created by Richard Bandler and John Grinder in California, United States, in the 1970s. It relates to the way we communicate with ourselves. 'Neuro' means 'of the mind', and 'linguistic' is the study of language. Therefore, NLP purely means that you can re-programme the language of your own mind – that is, the way that you think and the words you choose to think with.

Neil Long, licensed NLP practitioner, and voice and confidence coach, explains more about NLP:

NLP is an acronym for neuro-linguistic programming, which sounds rather complicated – don't worry though; it really is not, particularly for our purposes here. It's a form of psychology that, rather than focusing on WHY people are the way they are, focuses on something much more immediate and useful – HOW they are the way they are inside their mind, to create the experience and results they are getting.

NLP has been described as the instruction manual for the mind that you should have been given at birth, with a set of techniques for personal growth and change. It involves a good understanding of how the mind works (which is actually quite mechanical); rather than trying to fix what's wrong, it focuses on people who are competent in certain skills, and how they do that (what is going on in their head to create that result), and teaching those same skills to others, so they can replicate the results, in a process called 'modelling'.

NLP holds the premise that we all have the resources within us to make any change we want, but sometimes we do not realise what

*we are capable of – or, in NLP terms, our map of the world is some-
what small – so an NLP practitioner will focus on giving people more
choice, not less adding to, not taking away; indeed, expanding their
map of the world, so they have a greater range from which to select
when they make their choices.*

*The programming reference likens the mind to a computer, in the
sense that it does not matter how long the program has been running,
when it is removed the output of the computer will change every time.
Therefore, with the right strategy at the right time, NLP can work
fast and powerfully. It is not that the practitioner is zapping you with
some kind of angel magic dust; more that they have skilfully guided
you to your own power, resources, wisdom and creativity.*

*As I say, you will end up with a basic understanding of your mind.
Note a BASIC understanding is all you need – I do not need to know
the exact workings of the engine in my car to operate it effectively and
neither do you need an in-depth understanding of the neurology of
your brain to operate it effectively to get the results you want.*

*In the same way, all I need to do is understand how a steering wheel
basically works, and I can get my car to go where I want it to. But
let's say the steering lock is on and I am stuck – all I need do is to
have a basic understanding to take the lock off; then the whole thing
works as it is supposed to. It is the same with your mind. We will take
the 'steering lock' off, to enable sufferers to point their mind in the
direction they want.*

*Does the sufferer have a part in this? Yes. And they would not want it
any other way in my opinion. The beauty here is that they will be put in
charge, 'at cause' if I may, rather than being 'at effect' of their experience.
In other words, they are not a victim. And that's a good thing, isn't it?*

*As you might surmise, NLP is used for many different applications,
therapeutically for helping people change their eating habits or lose
weight, for removing phobias in a very short time, or for helping people improve their self-esteem. It is even used in sales to increase them.*

A little more about the mind

You may have heard the phrase, 'I'm in two minds about it.' Well, that's actually quite accurate! We all have a conscious and unconscious mind. They both have unique qualities. The conscious mind holds our rational nature, where we make decisions, decide what to have for dinner, develop a business strategy etc.

However, the unconscious mind operates on automatic. It does not stop and think 'Hmm, maybe that's not such a good idea'; it just does what is needed. So, if you think about a past, good experience, the chances are that good feelings will come to the forefront of your mind quickly and automatically.

It's the conscious mind that steps in and stops us doing silly things – to use our driving example, the conscious mind will decide to drive safely, observing the rules of the road, keeping to the speed limits. Meanwhile the unconscious mind will be processing all the relevant millions and millions of bits of data and paring it all down to a small enough chunk that the conscious mind can process. (The conscious mind can only hold five to seven pieces of information at one time – that's why phone numbers are written in chunks rather than one long number.) The unconscious is one massive storehouse of all out memories and experiences.

Back to our driving example; let's say that the car ahead of me suddenly brakes. I do not 'stop and think'; I just press the brake and slow down. 'Without thinking'. Automatically, you see.

Now it is a wonderful thing in many ways that we have an autopilot – if we didn't we would have to think about how to open a door every time we encountered one, not to mention beat our hearts, digest our food and do all the other functions of our body that we all take for granted. A mammoth task!

What does not serve us is when habits of thought that are not useful to us become automatic, perhaps so automatic we think, 'That's just the way it is.' The good news is that such thinking can be changed.

The unconscious works also by repetition to learn something, and operates under the instructions of the conscious mind, which is the bit of you that you know as you.

Therefore, you are in charge, and in control. No more victim of anything. You never were.

How does NLP work with OCD?

There are a number of techniques that can be used in the treatment of OCD, ranging from distraction to deliberate use of attention, re-training the mind and reassigning the importance you give to your own thoughts. All of these things are naturally done by the person who does not have OCD, and the good news is, it can be taught.

NLP can help the person suffering find the root cause of their OCD symptoms, helping to alter the thought patterns that are driving them. It's based on the belief that change can be accomplished much more quickly if the unconscious mind is challenged.

Similar to most forms of OCD treatment, NLP encourages the person suffering to break the vicious cycle of the compulsive rituals. It can be difficult to differentiate between what is happening in reality, and what is happening in your mind. To change these thoughts and break the power that they have over the sufferer, NLP can work to show the sufferer how to think differently and change their unconscious thought processes at a deeper level.

This happens by targeting the 'belief systems' that are apparent in many OCD sufferers. They often are unable to shake the feeling that something bad is going to happen unless they engage in compulsive rituals. In this sense, the intention is to re-programme the sufferer's mind so that their unconscious thought processes are no longer in control.

Ursula talks of her experience with NLP:

> My journey through my NLP treatment really made a positive change in my life. It helped me change the way I think, and gave me the tools to be able to manage my OCD better.

Hypnotherapy

Largely owing to the way hypnosis is described and presented by the media, there is a great deal of myth and misconception surrounding it. For a large majority, the word 'hypnosis' conjures up visions of magician-type performers persuading unwitting volunteers that they are a chicken / can fly / have an otter in their trousers. We are led to believe that hypnosis involves the total surrender of one person's will to another, who is then free to manipulate their hypnotised subject in any way they please.

In reality, hypnosis is simply a deep (and very pleasant) state of relaxation. It can be compared to when we awake on a weekend morning and have nothing to leap out of bed for; we tend simply to lie still and enjoy the sensation of being somewhere between sleep and total alertness. We would still be able to jump to attention in the event of an emergency, and we are aware of the thoughts that drift in and out of our minds. It is this state which hypnosis exactly replicates.

Dionne Curtis, a hypnotherapist, NLP practitioner and TFT practitioner (see page 67), explains what is hypnotherapy:

The history of hypnosis goes back to the 1800s and the technique has been used to better people's lives in many ways since; this is done by communicating with the subconscious part of your mind to effect changes that you want to happen. It is recognised that only 10 per cent of our brain's function is done consciously, which leaves 90 per cent done sub- or unconsciously. The therapist works with the subconscious mind to create positive change.

Chapter 4

Hypnotherapy is a form of psychotherapy used to create subconscious change in a client in the form of new responses, thoughts, attitudes, behaviours or feelings. It is undertaken with a subject in hypnosis. The client is in a trance-like state where their body is deeply relaxed but their mind is active. We all go into such states of mind naturally in daily life – for example, when daydreaming or concentrating deeply on something.

The client stays in control at all times; they may have feelings of lightness or heaviness – there are various possibilities. When the client is in a relaxed state the hypnotherapist suggests things that might help the client change their behaviour or relieve their symptoms. The client's conscious mind switches off whilst they are relaxed and their unconscious mind is then open to the positive suggestions of the therapist.

The therapist works with clients to change their behaviour in a positive way and to reduce physical symptoms.

Dionne explains how hypnotherapy works for treating OCD:

Hypnosis is used for OCD and it works by changing the mind-set of the sufferer and easing the anxiety symptoms.

Hypnotherapy changes the client's thinking so that they can take control of their OCD. This is important as many OCD sufferers feel that the OCD is controlling them. Hypnotherapy enables the client to make the distinction between what they feel is true – that is, 'all the locks are open', or 'my hands are full of germs' – and what the actual truth is – 'all the locks are closed', or 'my hands are clean and not full of germs'. This is done in two ways:

a) *OCD sufferers can be shown how to consciously think in a different way about their behaviours.*

b) *the therapist can change the thoughts and feeling of the client at an unconscious level, eliminating old behaviours and creating new lines of thought and therefore new behaviour patterns.*

Paul tells us about how hypnotherapy helped with his OCD:

I had hypnotherapy which really cleared out my head and allowed me to start again. I do still have many of the rituals, but they are grounded now in positive actions – I don't think you can always stop these but you can channel them by changing your ultimate goal and letting your brain find new ways to get there – as long as the ultimate goal is positive the brain will find the way for you.

Counselling

The word 'counselling' covers a multitude of different disciplines. Often counsellors use elements of psychotherapy, CBT and NLP within their method. Most broadly, however, counselling offers an opportunity for clients to talk. Within an anonymous and safe environment, they are afforded the opportunity to speak about anything, while being gently guided with questions by their therapist, which allows them to come to important realisations about the origin and nature of their illness.

Counselling has a number of benefits for OCD sufferers. Firstly, it allows them to feel valued. People suffering from OCD and other mental health issues often feel isolated and misunderstood. Counselling provides a forum for them to explore their feelings. Secondly, counselling is, by its very nature, tailored to the individual. There is no set format for counsellors, which means that they must, to some extent, treat everyone's case individually. As such, it is crucial in counselling, perhaps more so than in any other type of therapy, to find the right 'fit' in terms of a practitioner. A good counsellor should make their patient feel safe, secure and valued at all times. They should establish a bond of trust with their clients and make it easy for them to discuss potentially painful or difficult issues.

Chapter 4

As a mental health counsellor myself, I ensure I have met with a sufferer's parents or carers before I commence working with them, if they are under 18. Many people are surprised that I insist on this, but I have always been of the opinion that rehabilitating an OCD sufferer, or someone with any other mental health illness, is a group effort and one which will involve constant communication between clients and the people who are most influential in their life. If a patient is over 18 and has approached me independently, I usually bring carers into the process a little further into therapy. Under the Data Protection Act, I of course have to gain the client's permission to share information with carers. Once I have explained the paramount importance of trust and communication, this permission is normally granted.

I like the families of my clients to understand my methods and the work I will undertake with their loved ones, so that they can be as helpful and supportive as possible throughout the recovery process. Recovery can sometimes be long, with the sufferer's mind-set changing at each stage, sometimes on a day-by-day basis.

It is important that carers are aware of the changes to help them to gain a real insight into how their loved one is thinking and feeling at each juncture within the process. This is why I prefer to keep them in the loop.

Before a client sees me for the first time, I research their interests, whether these are film, music, clothes or various hobbies; this enables me to be able to establish a rapport with them during their first session. It is important for sufferers to feel understood and accepted. It is also crucial they perceive themselves as a three-dimensional person, rather than as simply 'a mental health issue'. OCD can envelope the identity of the sufferer. By talking to my clients about their hobbies, interests and passions, I am demonstrating to them that they are individuals who are not defined by their illness. This puts into motion the journey towards my clients envisaging life without their issue – a huge leap in terms of the recovery process.

Encouraging clients to acknowledge their struggles and open up about the factors which might have influenced them is not always easy – it requires time, patience and perseverance. I tend to work very intensively with my clients initially, seeing them two or three times a week. The challenge to negative emotions and feelings should be worked through as swiftly as possible. This also helps to quickly establish a bond of trust and friendship during this time. Eventually this can be maintained with less frequent sessions.

Michelle, mother of a past client, Milly, says:

My daughter was struggling with OCD as she challenged anorexia nervosa, and was controlling her life in the world of OCD with excessive rituals. By this time, we had left the NHS CAMHS (Child and Adolescent Mental Health Services) support service as they were completely cold, uncaring and insensitive to our family, and our daughter had no hope with them; she was never going to connect with them I took the decision to get rid of them from her life as they were causing more harm than good. When we discovered Lynn, we discovered hope! Simple. Lynn cares and she really got to know our daughter, loved her like her own and showed her a way forward, with little steps, challenging rituals a bit at a time. But it was the constant calm and encouragement that we got from Lynn, always at the end of the phone if we needed her with kind words and a strength that was never present in the NHS. Would I recommend her way of counselling? YES – 100 per cent. We have our daughter back and she has been given coping mechanisms to last her life through.

Milly describes her experience:

I developed OCD following anorexia nervosa and had to do certain things in certain ways at certain times. It was a way of delaying eating when I look back. Lynn showed me so much love and support; she was kind and talked to me like I mattered and she really wanted me to get better. She helped me challenge timings and repeated rituals, and would always text me back if I was worried. Every other person I met through the illness in the NHS – doctors, counsellors etc – were just doing a job; they were cold, miserable and didn't really ever try to find out about the real me. Lynn really cared and made me feel like I had a voice and was supported – nothing was too much trouble. Lynn Crilly and her strength are the reason I am well, completely recovered, together with my family support, and I will always be grateful that we found her. She is a very special person. My fairy Godmother.

Counselling is, ultimately, the client's journey. It is important that the people I work with look forward and want to come to their sessions. Each client's therapy is adapted to their individual requirements, as I find this helps them to relax and feel more at ease, thereby enabling them to engage with me and make progress in their therapy. All the techniques I use help to reinforce a client's own desire to get better. If they do not have this desire, counselling may then stabilise their condition but it cannot move them forward. It is important to remember that as the counselling journey is unique to each client, so is the recovery process.

Thought field therapy (TFT)

TFT was developed by Roger Callahan in the USA. It is the practice of tapping in a set sequence (algorithm) on acupuncture pressure points to realign meridian energies (see Figure 1 and description on pages 71-3) within the body to promote internal healing. Dionne Curtis, a hypnotherapist, NLP practitioner and TFT practitioner, explains the technique of TFT and how it can help OCD:

There are set programmes within the mind of each of us that cover every emotion, even though each individual responds in a different way from the next. Some people manifest anger, for example, by repressing it; others give full vent to their anger by becoming violent or tearful. TFT interrupts the programme between experiencing the emotion and responding to it when the response to that emotion is inappropriate or disproportionate – for example, crying when angry can be a release and healthy, but sobbing uncontrollably to a point where it is negatively affecting life is a disproportionate response.

With OCD, the obsessions are negative thoughts, impulses, persistent ideas or images which repeatedly come to mind; people having them often feel that they are inappropriate and intrusive and they can cause distress or anxiety. Compulsions are repetitive behaviours done in order to prevent or reduce the sufferer's anxiety or distress and to manage obsessive thoughts. TFT is effective for this type of illness as it interrupts the programme in the mind and alters the emotional response; there may also be other factors to the OCD that the therapist will be able to address during treatment.

What makes TFT different from other treatments/therapies is that the clients are shown how to treat themselves. They are given the correct meridian points to tap and in what order. This has two effects: the client is less inclined to become dependent on the therapist, but, more importantly, it gives the OCD sufferer the realisation that they are in control of their own treatment and that they are playing a fundamental part in their own recovery. This is particularly helpful when the client faces difficult situations in the future – they have a procedure to follow and the expertise to carry out their own treatment whenever they need it, which is hugely empowering.

Whilst TFT is an extremely quick form of treatment, the client still needs to invest time and be committed to following the practice. There is no 'quick fix' solution.

Grahame shares his positive experience of TFT:

> I visited Dionne for my struggles with OCD. My doctor had diagnosed me and wanted to put me on a low dose of medication, but I wanted to try some alternative therapies first and had heard about TFT through a mutual acquaintance. Dionne worked with me to help me believe that I could change my behaviours and that they were no longer serving me any good purpose. The TFT sessions worked well for me and I did not have to return to the doctor to get medication. I worked on creating time for relaxation so going forward I can recognise when I am getting over-stressed or anxious. I have memorised the sequence of tapping, so I can repeat the session we did together on my own.

Psychosensory techniques and principles (Psy TaP)

Kevin Laye, Harley Street-based therapy practitioner and founder of Psy TaP, whose current work is endorsed and supported by Paul McKenna, explains Psy TaP and how it can treat OCD successfully as follows:

In Psy TaP terms, we see OCD as an 'addiction pattern behaviour' (APB) issue.

OCD also varies in its severity, from something innocuous, like always having to have the TV volume set on an even number, right through to catastrophising thoughts that if a specific behaviour is not carried out we could come to harm, or someone we care for could come to harm, or, at the extreme end, we could even die.

I find a good exercise for people to do to understand the impulse people have to carry out a particular behaviour is as follows:
- *open your eyes wide and look ahead, without blinking...*
- *hold your eyes open for as long as you can and do not blink*
- *eventually you will reach a point where you do blink. At that*

moment, when you cannot, not blink... that is the impulse felt by someone with OCD or any APB... just as you must blink, they must do the behaviour.

My belief, though, is that unlike most addiction behaviours, there is another element to OCD, and it is that of safety, or even survival. I think different areas of the brain are at work with OCD too. In most addictions, it is the area of the brain called the nucleus accumbens and, more specifically, the right caudate nucleus, which will drive the behaviour. In OCD it seems the limbic system is also activated, which indicates a level of survival instinct and seeking safety is at play. This is perhaps why OCD is a more complex behaviour pattern to treat than a more conventional addiction.

In Psy TaP, we tend to use a blend of proven methodologies to treat OCD, from thought field therapy (TFT) meridian tapping techniques (see pages 67 and 72-3), to pattern-interrupt techniques (which de-link triggers and stop chain reactions at their starting point), to create a calm state by which the stresses caused by the fear of not doing the behaviour are diminished or sometimes deleted. Once this has been done and the behaviour has been either significantly diminished or removed, we then need to replace it with a new behaviour pattern. We call this process 'Avoid A-Void'. It is imperative we do this step to prevent old patterns from re-establishing themselves. We sometimes frame it that they use their OCD tendencies but to a more productive end so they become focused on doing things with a more positive intent and more productive outcomes. We find this eliminates the fear of 'what is my identity' or 'who will I be' without my OCD behaviour. We negotiate with the non-conscious and thank it for what it has done to date, but ask it to use the same effort and energy on something more productive for the sufferer. It is rare not to get an agreement on this.

So how would a Psy TaP treatment protocol go in a session with someone presenting with OCD? First we would take a full history, including any associated significant emotional life events (we do *this because on many occasions the OCD has developed as a pattern following a trauma), and also any medications, both prescribed and self-prescribed, together with dosages. We would then begin to structure a treatment plan.*

TFT meridian tapping techniques *have a high success rate with OCD so this is a 'go to' technique. We obtain on a scale of 1-10 (the Wolpe scale) from the patient their current level of the issue when they think of the OCD 'now', with 10 being the greatest and 1 the least. This brings the issue from long-term memory into working memory and activates any perturbations. We then ask the patient to tap on a sequence of points (the 'meridian points') on their body as shown in Figure 1 (see next page).*

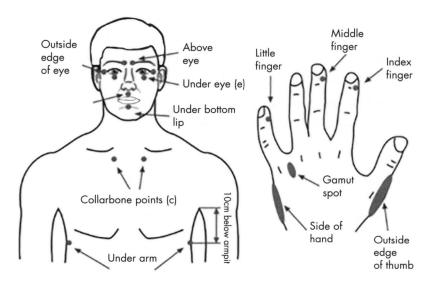

Figure 1: The meridian points for TFT

For OCD we begin with the following sequence:

    Tap the collarbone, point (c), five to 10 times

    Tap under the eye, point (e), five to 10 times

    Tap the collarbone, point (c), five to 10 times

Check the scale from 1-10 again. If the number has reduced, which means things are improving, we do the following sequence, whilst tapping what we call the 'Gamut spot' on the back of the hand (see Figures 1 and 2) continuously. (On very rare occasions there is no improvement; these are more complex cases and need more diagnostic work to treat successfully.)

1. Eyes open
2. Eyes closed
3. Eyes open down to right
4. Eyes open down to left
5. Eyes in a circle
6. Eyes in a circle – opposite direction
7. Hum a tune out loud
8. Count to five out loud
9. Hum a tune out loud

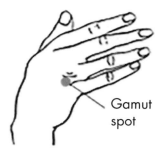

Gamut
spot

Figure 2: Gamut spot for TFT and the gamut treatment sequence

Again, we check on the scale of 1-10 feelings about OCD, and if these have reduced more we repeat:

Tap the collarbone, point (c), five to 10 times

Tap under the eye, point (e), five to 10 times

Tap the collarbone, point (c), five to 10 times

We then obtain a final number on the 1-10 scale.

TFT has been shown to be successful with over 80 per cent of our clients presenting with OCD using this generic code.

In Psy TaP we also teach a simple finger-squeeze method to generate pattern interrupts for specific trigger emotions. (A 'pattern interrupt' is like turning off a thought before it develops into a feeling or an emotion; if the thought is inactive, you cannot have

the feeling or emotion – a bit like asking someone to tell you about a book they have not read.) Prime emotions associated with OCD are fear and anxiety (panic). We teach clients to squeeze the index and middle fingers together and hold them for a few seconds and try to generate the feelings of fear and the anxiety. You will often see a surprised look on their face when they are unable to tune into and generate these feelings. These emotional trigger points are shown in Figure 3.

Figure 3: Mapping the hand to emotions

We believe, based on experience and feedback from many hundreds of practitioners who have done thousands of treatments, that by continually and rapidly utilising this 'pattern interrupt' with the finger squeezing, the neuroplasticity effect will kick in and the neural pathways which are no longer able to fire will die back in a process known as 'synaptic pruning'. This will enable the newer and more productive, non-harmful, more positive and effective neural behaviour pathways (as Hebbs law states, 'What fires together, wires together') to develop and grow stronger, so the old behaviour restructures organically until it no longer needs to be managed, but it is the new way of functioning. This is organic change at work and not management or suppression of an emotion.

Then to 'future pace' (imagine the self in a desired situation in the future) and generate new behaviour patterns we use the following exercise.

Positive imagery exercise

Raise the right hand up and to the right of you so you are looking up at it... Look into your palm and create a compelling image of what you want to be like, assuming that nothing can fail. Then double the intensity of the picture and brighten it. Then double it again and again... When it looks amazing, and only then, take a deep breath in and as you exhale pull the image into your chest and absorb it through your heart; then as you breathe in, intensify the image and as you exhale again, drive the feeling through your body into every cell, muscle, nerve, fibre and tissue until you are saturated with the good feeling. Then repeat with another good image.

Do this as often as you like. After all, who can never have enough good feelings?

This is just a sample of one of the multitude of options we have available within the Psy TaP discipline.

Bodytalk

Bodytalk is a holistic therapy, meaning that it is concerned primarily with the relationship between body and mind, but is not limited to this. Understanding the significance of the part the emotions play in a person's wellbeing, Bodytalk literally works on every level of the human being and excludes nothing.

Established in the mid-1990s by Dr John Veltheim, Bodytalk describes itself as an 'integrative system' which taps into the 'innate wisdom' of the body to determine health problems that may be present, and to treat them. Dr Veltheim has a background in acupuncture and chiropractic, and has developed the Bodytalk system to include the best the West has to offer, married with the wisdom of Eastern practices.

Bodytalk hinges on the philosophy that the body is comprised of various energy systems designed to work in harmony. During periods of sickness – physical, mental or emotional – these energies can be enormously compromised, resulting in a complete imbalance in one or all of these areas.

While this might seem a little 'alternative' for some, the success of Bodytalk as an element in OCD treatment is extremely effective. This might be because sufferers are encouraged to establish a bond of trust with their body once more, so, just as with NLP, they take responsibility for their own health. In eating disorder patients, the mind and body are at war, so Bodytalk primarily attempts to open paths of communication between them, hopefully bringing harmony back to the partnership.

Kyra Mathers, whose daughter was a client of mine, has gone on to train as a Bodytalk practitioner. She has an unshakeable belief in the effectiveness of the therapy for treating mental illness, saying:

> One of the benefits of Bodytalk is the fact that clients do not have to identify their issues themselves. A skilled Bodytalk practitioner is able to establish areas of the body–mind complex that are out of balance and re-establish harmony within them. Often, in the initial stages at least, OCD sufferers are reluctant to open up and discuss their lives and habits with, for example, a counsellor, yet with Bodytalk, you don't have to speak at all if you don't want to.

Of course, Bodytalk may 'throw up an issue which then needs to be dealt with'. (These are likely to be psychological elements of the sufferer's condition.) The patient may then need to go on to use a different therapy in conjunction with Bodytalk. Kyra is of the opinion that NLP is a particularly effective companion therapy for Bodytalk, so that the body and mind are targeted simultaneously. She summarises by saying:

> In hindsight, Bodytalk helped alleviate my daughter's stress and improve her mood, so enabling her to respond more effectively to Lynn's counselling.

Laura Forbes is a Bodytalk practitioner who believes the therapy to be cutting-edge, describing it as:

> ... one of the only truly holistic forms of bodywork in the world today. Practitioners are trained to identify 'energy blockages' in the body which signify ill-health within the 'physical, emotional, mental and spiritual layers of the human make-up.

In this way, Bodytalk could be described as a 'blend of Eastern and Western philosophies', so creating a powerful therapy.

Laura has used Bodytalk to treat OCD sufferers, but concedes that it is most effective when used 'alongside other types of therapy in a team approach to recovery'. She adds, 'It is widely recognised that [OCD] can be linked to control, which Bodytalk can help to balance, as well as establishing the reasons for this need.'

Medication

Medication can be used alone or alongside most other forms of therapy. It can help to alleviate some of the anxiety surrounding the OCD, making it more manageable. It has been described by some sufferers as 'taking the edge off' the unease that is often linked to a person's OCD.

Natasha shares how medication has helped her:

> Medication has helped to lift my mood, so I am more able to deal with the thoughts. It doesn't fix things, but it makes the OCD more manageable and puts you on more of an even keel to be able to cope with the thoughts a bit more easily.

The most common group of medications prescribed for OCD are 'selective serotonin reuptake inhibitors' (SSRIs). They are thought to work by controlling imbalances in levels of serotonin, a chemical in the brain that sends messages between brain cells (a 'neurotransmitter'). Serotonin is thought to be involved in regulating many aspects of mental health from anxiety, to memory, to sleep (in the form melatonin).

Often, SSRIs are referred to as 'antidepressants' as they are commonly used for, and can be successful in, the treatment of depression. They are recommended for the treatment of OCD by the National Institute of Health and Social Care Excellence (NICE) – an independent body set up by the government in 1999 to produce best-practice guidelines in healthcare. According to a study published in Stanford Medicine online,[5] 40–60 per cent of sufferers saw marked improvement in how they could manage their OCD when taking an SSRI drug.

It is important to remember that everyone is an individual, and although some medication can be very effective, one person may respond better than another. However, as there is a variety of SSRI medications available on the market, often there can be a 'trial and error' phase to decide the most effective drug for that person.

Medication is not always a quick fix as it can take up to 12 weeks to start feeling any benefits; however, if the sufferer is experiencing depression as well, they may feel the effects more quickly.

The most popular drugs prescribed, and approved by the NICE guidelines, to treat adults with OCD are: fluoxetine, fluvoxamine, paroxetine, sertraline and citalopram. However, a doctor may prescribe other antidepressants or psychiatric medications, depending on the age of the sufferer and what s/he feels may work best for the sufferer.

As with most medications, each one can have a variety of side effects, so it is always advisable, before starting, to read the information leaflet provided. This will help the sufferer and their carers understand the possible changes that may be experienced as the drug begins to get into their system, and hopefully starts to work beneficially.

Medication should always be monitored by a doctor or GP, and the risks and benefits explained. Do not be afraid to ask any questions about anything you are unsure of with regards to the medication. Should you notice any drastic changes in the sufferer's behaviour, or severe side effects, you should recommend that they consult their doctor immediately.

My Samantha tells us of her experience with medication:

From a young age I have always been anti-medication, as I was always stubborn enough to think I could sort everything out on my own as well as being afraid of what effect it might have on me and whether I would be able to control it! I then hit the rock bottom of my OCD, when it was either sink or swim. I knew I was drowning in the deep end and needed a little help to the surface. I thought to myself I had nothing to lose; I was already at my lowest; maybe this time around I needed to put my shield down and try it. From my own experience, the medication I took didn't change my personality, I wasn't out of control. I had just been freed slightly from the burdening voices. By no means did it get rid of them completely, it just pushed them from the front of my head, to the back; I could still hear them but was able to distinguish more what were my thoughts and what were those of the illness. It gave me more definition and a clearer path to recovery.

There is no 'correct' or 'right' path to recovery. You may find either a single treatment or a combination of treatments works best for the sufferer. The important thing to remember is that there is, without doubt, a form of treatment available that can help your loved one overcome their OCD. If one treatment is not working, do not be afraid to change track, and try another. It can be quite common to try various therapies before you find the right treatment for the individual sufferer. Your loved one showing a willingness to get better is a huge step forward, and sometimes it can be frustrating and challenging for carers and sufferers when there is a delay in finding an effective treatment. I hope this chapter has assisted you in making sense of some of the terms, buzz-words and theories and will aid you in making an informed decision about what to try next, always remembering that recovery is possible.

At the back of this book you will find an index of resources and practitioners, all of whom I have personally worked with, researched and / or spoken to at great length about the treatments and methods they offer.

Chapter 5

OCD and wellbeing

In addition to treatments, which may be effective singly or in combination, it is essential that sufferers – and their carers – also make positive efforts to improve their wellbeing. In today's pressured world this is important for everybody, but at no time more so than when combating a mental health problem. In this chapter I look at a range of elements that can improve wellbeing and give the treatments you may choose from Chapter 4 the best chance of helping.

We live in an age where what was once considered alternative treatment is now becoming much more mainstream and widely accepted. I would encourage you, the reader, to be open-minded towards all the avenues potentially leading to recovery, both conventional and so-called 'alternative' treatments that are available to you. The approaches described below are not mutually exclusive to conventional treatment, but can work successfully hand in hand with it, thereby aiding healing for the sufferer and, in some cases, the carer as well. It goes without saying that basic self-care is of paramount importance, including getting the right amount of sleep (page 87), exercise (see next) and good nutrition (page 90). This has been borne out by my own experience, both personally and professionally.

I have asked specialists within each field, all of whom I know personally, to help give you an understanding of how their individual discipline can help mental wellbeing for both carers and sufferers alike.

Exercise

Exercise is good for the mind, body and spirit.

People who exercise regularly tend to do so because it gives them a greater sense of wellbeing. They tend to have more energy throughout the day, sleep better at night and have sharper memories, and most tend to feel more relaxed and positive about themselves and their lives.

Activity and exercise are especially important for people living with mental illness, not least because people who have mental illness often have a higher risk of physical illness also. Similarly, people with physical illnesses can be at a higher risk of developing mental illness, such as depression, anxiety, disordered eating and OCD. The body and mind exist in balance, directly affecting one another.

Tan, an experienced personal trainer, adds:

There is such a strong link between physical activity and mental wellbeing that it simply cannot be ignored. Taking part in regular exercise reduces anxiety and depression whilst improving self-esteem, confidence and overall quality of life. Whether it's going to the gym or being outdoors, with friends and family or a personal trainer, exercise can play a vital part in maintaining health in both body and mind.

Scientists in research studies[6] have discovered that exercise causes the brain to release chemicals, including endorphins, which can make you feel energised and positive. One important chemical that is boosted is serotonin, the same component that is enhanced by antidepressants (see page 78)

– but without the side effects! Regular exercise can promote all kinds of changes in the brain, including neural growth, reduced inflammation, and new activity patterns that aid feelings of calm and wellbeing.

Exercise can also serve as a distraction, allowing the person to find some 'time out' to enable them to break out of the cycle of their negative and distractive thoughts that feed their mental illness.

My Samantha found exercise extremely beneficial, mentally and physically, throughout her recovery process. She worked with a highly experienced personal trainer, Jess, on a regular basis, who had a great understanding of mental illness, which meant that she was able to monitor Samantha's progress closely throughout.

Jess, a qualified personal trainer, speaks of their journey together:

My first impression of Sam when she began training with me was of a quiet and unsure young girl. She was trying to be positive and bravely showed me a picture of what she wanted to achieve – a healthy, shapely body – but I could tell she was hesitant to believe that she could manage it. Watching her progress and improve was not only a physical journey. As her body grew stronger she grew stronger mentally, more positive and confident, not only in the gym but also outside of it. She regained her appetite, both for food and for life.

Samantha adds:

Training has helped me build a strong, fit, healthy body that I am mentally in love with and physically know is the foundation that will help me conquer the world!

Mental and emotional benefits of exercise

- **More energy:** Increasing the heart rate several times a week will help the person to have more energy.
- **Stronger resilience:** When faced with mental or emotional challenges in life, exercise can help a person cope in a healthy way, instead of turning to alcohol, drugs or other negative behaviours that will ultimately make the person feel worse. Regular exercise can also help boost the immune system and reduce the impact of stress.
- **Sleep better:** Even small amounts of exercise at regular intervals can help to regulate sleep patterns.
- **Self-esteem:** Regular activity can improve the mind, body and soul. When it becomes part of everyday life, it can foster a sense of self-worth and make the person feel strong and powerful. They will feel better about how they look and, by meeting personal goals, will gain a sense of achievement.
- **Sharper memory and thinking:** The same endorphins that make a person feel positive, can also help with concentration, and improve the sharpness of the person's mentality for the tasks at hand. Exercise also stimulates the growth of new brain cells and helps prevent age-related decline.

Leanne Poyner, physical education specialist, personal performance and life coach, adds:

Taking part in a physical activity will not only benefit your physical health, but also your mental health and your social wellbeing. Together these three elements will help an individual to lead a balanced, positive lifestyle. Physical activity releases hormones that help a person to feel good and be able to think clearly and can also reduce stress. When you are feeling positive you have more energy and are more likely to be open to new opportunities that come your way, e.g.

career, social events. For someone who is suffering from OCD, exercise is an excellent way to focus the mind and channel the frustrations into something else.

A person does not need to devote hours and hours of their day to exercise, or train at a gym, sweat buckets, or run mile after mile after mile to reap the benefits. They can obtain all the physical and mental health benefits with 30 minutes of moderate exercise (that could be activities such as brisk walking, cycling, basketball) five times a week, or even two 15-minute exercise sessions five times per week will work equally well.

Someone suffering from OCD or any other mental health issues may find it difficult to take the first step into exercise. Here are some common barriers and some way in which they can be overcome.

- **Feeling overwhelmed:** When a person feels stressed, anxious or low, the thought of adding another obligation can seem overwhelming or even impossible. It is important to remember that physical activity helps us to do more and cope with things better. So, try to think of exercise as a priority and find ways to fit small amounts into everyday life.
- **Feeling exhausted:** When a person is tired and lethargic, it can feel as though taking exercise will make things worse and is all too much effort. However, it is worth remembering that physical activity is a powerful energiser. Studies[7] have shown that regular exercise can dramatically reduce fatigue and increase energy levels. The best place to start is at the beginning – for example, a person can go for a five-minute walk around the block or up and down the road, with the idea of increasing the time by a minute or two on each occasion. As they start to feel the benefit from it, it will hopefully not be a chore but an enjoyment.

- **Feeling hopeless:** Even if a person is starting at rock bottom they can still work out. Exercise helps people to get into shape. If they have no experience of exercising, they should start slowly, with a low-impact movement a few minutes each day, gradually building this up.
- **Feeling bad about yourself:** Most people are their own worst critic. No matter what the person's weight, age or fitness level, there are many others with the same goals of getting fit who feel the same. Being with people who are all in the same shoes can help. Perhaps the sufferer could take a class with people of a variety of fitness levels. Accomplishing even the smallest of fitness goals will help gain body confidence, which can only lead to the sufferer feeling better about him/herself.

One of the many people I have had the privilege to meet is the wonderful man, Frank Bruno. Over the years his own mental health issues have been well documented, and Frank has been very vocal about the importance of ongoing exercise as a contributory factor in the recovery process, and as part of everyday life and recommends:

> It was hard to exercise when on heavy medication. However, even a small amount every day, building up the time gradually – for example, starting by walking then running or going to the gym – is helpful. You don't have to be a body builder – look at it as part of your essential medication.

Having used exercise as part of his own recovery, Frank has gone on to start the Frank Bruno Foundation, which provides structured non-contact boxing sessions aimed at relieving the social, emotional and mental distress that adversely affects the mental health of children, young people and adults.

Exercise can be enjoyed in many ways – throwing a frisbee with a dog or a friend, walking around a shopping centre, cycling to work or simply going for a walk. Activities such as gardening or even doing small improvements to the house can be good ways to start moving around more. As well as helping to become more active, these activities can also leave the person with a sense of purpose and accomplishment.

However, at this point I must emphasise that exercise can have a negative effect in some instances, particularly in people with OCD and eating disorders, Some people with mental health issues can actually use exercise to fuel their illness. Exercise should never become an obsession.

A way to tell if someone is exercising excessively is firstly by monitoring how often they exercise. It is also important to monitor how the individual feels if their routine is changed. If they become anxious and panicked about missing a session of exercise, then their habit may have developed into an obsession, and outside intervention may be needed.

Exercise can also have a beneficial social component. Being part of a team or club can help a person to feel they have a sense of identity and belong to a network of people, united by their passion for a particular activity. Working as a team through sport can help to build self-confidence and self-belief as well, all of which has to be a much healthier way to socialise than via the internet!

Sleep

Sleep plays a vital part in good health and wellbeing throughout a person's life. Getting enough quality sleep at the right times can help to protect their mental and physical health, quality of life and overall safety. According to the National Sleep Foundation, for a person's overall health and wellbeing, school-age children (6-13 years) need approximately nine to 11 hours sleep per night, teens (14-17 years) need approximately eight to 10, and adults (18-64 years) need approximately seven to nine hours.

There is a close relationship between mental health and sleep. Many people who experience mental health issues also experience disturbed sleep patterns or insomnia. Over a long period of time, disturbed sleep can actually lead to a mental health condition or make an existing mental illness worse. With lack of sleep, the person may:

- experience lowered self-esteem through inability to cope
- experience social isolation
- struggle to deal with everyday life
- experience low mood
- experience low energy levels
- develop depression and/or anxiety
- experience an inability to carry out usual social activities
- have feelings of loneliness.

Most importantly, being constantly tired can affect a person's ability to rationalise anxieties and banish irrational thoughts. This can feed into negative thinking patterns which are often associated with OCD and other mental health issues.

This is echoed by Natasha, who says:

Sleep has been a huge contributory factor and I find tiredness to be one of my biggest triggers.

While some experts recommend that an adult should have between seven and nine hours of sleep a night (see above), others say that the *quality* of sleep is far more important than the quantity. For example, if a person has six hours of high-quality, uninterrupted sleep they will receive more benefit than having eight hours of restless, interrupted sleep.

Sleep is not just time out from people's busy routines; everyone needs sleep to help both their mind and body recover from the stresses of everyday life. Sleep is a healing process, one I cannot champion enough for people suffering from OCD and, indeed, any other mental illnesses.

Sleep has played a vital part in my daughter, Samantha's, recovery, as she says:

> Although sometimes I found it hard to get to sleep as my head was full up and could not think straight, I would listen to relaxation music which would help me to drown out the thoughts, making it easier to get to sleep. I found that having slept I would wake up feeling more refreshed. Sometimes if I was able I would have a nap during the day which I found really helped me to think more clearly too. Without sleep I did not have the energy and headspace to cope with and move past the thoughts. Sleep has been a major part in my recovery.

Getting a good night's sleep is crucial for both the sufferer and their carers alike. There are things that we can all do to help us achieve this:

- If possible get into a routine of going to sleep and waking up at the same time is ideal, although this is not realistic for everyone, I know.
- Develop a pre-bed routine, which may include having a bath, or reading or listening to relaxation music, getting the mind into a relaxed state; this should help one to drift off more easily.
- Allow no iPads, smart phones, television or electronic games in the bedroom. Some people experience disturbed sleep due to the use of technology in the bedroom and blue light from many devices enhances wakefulness. Going to bed and then spending time on these devices can stimulate the brain, making it more likely to wake up in the night and then have trouble getting back to sleep, due to feeling the need to check for messages, social media etc.
- Make sure the bedroom is dark and as quiet as possible, and the temperature is comfortably cool (but not cold).
- Alcohol and caffeine can also disturb sleep, as does rich food eaten late at night, so avoid these.

Having seen at first hand how regular, good-quality sleep has benefited Samantha, giving her the energy and strength she needed to be able to challenge and overcome the negative thoughts in her head, I cannot reiterate enough the power and importance of sleep and the vital role it plays in the recovery process from OCD and any other mental health issues.

Nutrition

I am sure, most of us have heard, or been told at some point, 'You are what you eat', but we may ask ourselves, what exactly does that mean? Put simply, food is fuel and raw materials – the types of food and drink you consume determine the nutrients in your system, and can affect how well your mind and body are able to function.

May Simpkin, registered personalised nutritionist, explains below in more detail:

Food plays a key role and it is vital to look at diet and consider whether there are any deficiencies that may be contributing to development of mood imbalances, as well as thinking about the management of mental health issues or prevention in the first place. The interactions between different nutrients are equally important. The brain works hard 24/7 and needs to be constantly fuelled from the foods we eat. Without this fuel, brain function will be affected and, ultimately, so will your mood.

According to the Mental Health Foundation, those who reported a mental health problem of any degree also reported a less healthy diet in terms of fresh fruit and vegetables and cooking from scratch, but included more unhealthy foods, such as crisps, chocolate, ready meals and takeaways. A systematic review, published in the American Journal of Clinical Nutrition *suggests that high intakes of fruit, vegetables, fish and wholegrains are associated with a reduced risk of depression (http://ajcn.nutrition.org/content/99/1/181.long).[8] It is no coincidence that the rise in mental health problems in the last 50 years has accompanied a rise in the consumption of processed foods and less fresh fruit and vegetables.*

Alongside medical intervention and professional treatment and guidance, a varied and healthy diet will go a long way to helping recovery, controlling mood and restoring balance.

Peggy (see page 12) champions good nutrition and says:

Eat good food. It isn't expensive – tuna, vegetables, pulses – cooking and meal planning, stocking a cupboard and a freezer are a great outlet for fusspots like me!

Yoga

Yoga is fast becoming a part of many people's everyday routine, with many feeling the benefits of it both mentally and physically. Speaking from experience, both the carer and the sufferer can potentially benefit greatly.

Yoga and massage specialist, Debbie Pennington, tells us more about yoga and how it can benefit OCD and mental health:

There have been several studies over the last 20 years in relation to the possible benefits of yoga to sufferers of OCD, and the results are very positive. Lifetime sufferers have even reported an immediate improvement, which is exceptional and exciting.

Yoga is not just an exercise class; it's a lifestyle, working on the whole body, asanas (postures), breathing techniques and meditation and maybe even result in a different way of looking at your life and life around you. The aim is to lead a holistic life. As you may know, 'holistic' means a balance of mind, body and spirit. These three components of each of us are interconnected and when one is impaired it has an effect on the whole. Practising yoga helps us to re-align and to bring a sense of calm, balance and self-worth back to us, among many other benefits. The process of meditation helps us to focus on something, such as our breathing, to start to eliminate the busy constant chatter of our minds. It's perfectly normal to have a never-ending stream of thoughts in our heads, but it's a fact that a lot of it is worry and non-positive thought. Many people find their OCD symptoms worsen when in a state of anxiety; yoga meditation sets us on a journey to start to look at our thoughts from a different perspective and then try to eliminate unhelpful thoughts and calm the mind, creating space and a sense of peace, even if just for a minute. These skills can then be taken through daily life by practising mindfulness in our daily activities. If suffering from mental health issues, such as OCD, these skills can be invaluable.

There are different types of yoga out there and it can be difficult or even daunting to know which to choose. Vanda Scaravelli-inspired yoga highlights the importance of being kind to yourself; this seems to be the obvious way forward to many of us. To make changes you need to listen to your body, going with it and not against it, and take the time to know yourself. It may be that no changes are to be made and we learn acceptance. It is not about pushing your body into that perfect textbook shape, but thinking about what needs to be released to move in a certain way and what needs to be engaged, and tadah! You have found yourself there, and found out something about the real you along the way.

The philosophy and theory of yoga were written down thousands of years ago and they have stood the test of time. GPs and medical organisations are recognising the benefits more and more, which is fantastic. Being yogic does not mean we are ignoring the pathological facts when we have problems like a mental illness, but that we are also recognising what cannot be seen and does not show on an X-ray. Alongside our human knowledge of anatomy, it all fits together and makes good sense. Let's try to address the root of a problem and not just treat the symptom or subdue it with pharmaceutical drugs.

When asked if there was anything else she would like to add, Debbie concluded:

There are so many benefits that result from the practice of yoga, it's difficult to summarise and so better that they are experienced. Quite often, on completion of an hour yoga class that incorporates relaxation, posture work, breathing and meditation, you will feel fulfilled, renewed, calm, happy and have a sense of self-worth. Try it for yourself, and don't worry – there is no need to feel self-conscious; nobody's judging you in yoga and all are welcome no matter their age or weight or ability. The more you do, the more apparent will be the benefits and results. One predominant word in yoga philosophy is ahimsa – I will try to explain this important term. Ahimsa *means 'maintain compassion towards yourself and others'. It means 'being kind and treating all things with care'. Embedded in the Vanda Scaravelli-inspired yoga, the principle of* ahimsa *is first and foremost related to ourselves. Ahimsa teaches that our yoga practice becomes our way of being in the world.*

Pauline, a carer of an OCD sufferer, tells us of her positive experience with yoga:

After a recommendation, I took up yoga a few years ago; I was really struggling mentally with looking after my son who has OCD. It took me a couple of classes to get into it, but now it has become part of my weekly routine, it is my 'me time' which takes my mind away to a different place.

Mindfulness

Life can, at times, be hectic, and it can be easy to rush through each day without stopping to appreciate the here-and-now. Paying more attention to the present moment – to your own thoughts and feelings, and to the world around you – can improve your mental wellbeing.

Some may call this awareness 'mindfulness'.

Catherine Kell, a child therapist and parent coach, explains what mindfulness is:

Mindfulness is a way of training the mind to be 'present'. It is a secular meditative practice which involves being aware of your own moment-to-moment experience and doing so with an attitude of kindness, acceptance, compassion and non-judgement. When we learn to observe our thoughts and feelings, and not engage with them or try to change them, we can create space to respond rather than react. It is in this space that we can break the cycle of our habitual reactions and patterns of thinking, and this has huge significance for maintaining mental health.

When asked how mindfulness can benefit mental health, Catherine says:

Mindfulness can have a really positive effect on mental health and general wellbeing, and more and more studies are now being conducted to gain longer-term evidence of this. For example, for people suffering from recurrent depression, studies have shown that following their participation in a full mindfulness-based cognitive therapy (MBCT) programme, they are less likely to experience future depressive relapses. Details of studies and ongoing clinical, peer-reviewed research in various mindfulness-based interventions can be found easily online and specifically at the Oxford Mindfulness Centre at www. oxfordmindfulness.org

I know from my own work with children and adolescents that the teaching of mindfulness has been beneficial to their mental health in a wide range of areas, such as strengthening awareness, attention, focus, emotion-regulation, appreciation, resilience and also alleviating stress, 'nerves', worry, ruminative thoughts and anxiety. Mindfulness can also benefit sleep. For some, mindfulness is completely transformative in terms of ending painful cycles of depression or compulsive behaviours. Not only can mindfulness improve mental health, but, importantly, the learning of mindful-

ness techniques also provides a person with tools and practices to enable themselves to maintain good mental health, to stay well. Skills such as learning to unlock the mind from negative over-thinking, over-analysing and rumination, as well as recognising the patterns of thinking that cause unhappiness, can last a lifetime.

Lilly shares her experience of mindfulness and how it has helped her:

> Having struggled with OCD for several years and tried many different therapies, mindfulness is the one thing that has helped me to see things and certain situations differently.

Drama and the Arts

I have seen at first hand how participating in drama has enhanced the sense of self and mental wellbeing of my own daughter. Samantha began doing drama workshops at our local theatre when she was well into the recovery process, but still felt there was 'something missing'. Being a naturally shy person, drama gave Samantha the safe place she needed to explore emotions. It has completely transformed the way she sees herself and her communication skills and has given her the confidence she so desperately needed. In some ways, I would say that it is drama and finally finding herself through it that has helped strengthen her recovery from mental illness.

Actor and coach, Dave Spinx, kick-started Samantha's renewed love of drama. He says:

> When I first met Sam, I quickly realised that I was dealing with someone who was uncertain and unclear about who she really was. There was a lack of confidence and direction and I felt that it would take something special to get her on the right road. I was only there to teach drama, but in our

one-to-one sessions it clearly became drama therapy as well. That special something came from Sam herself. From learning how to listen, questioning her decisions and reaching inside for the right answers, she soon became a different person from the isolated young lady whom I first met. Who would have thought that just a few years down the road she would be completing a full-time drama degree with a whole new future in front of her. I now see a confident and healthy, beautiful young woman – someone who showed the willingness and had the courage to step outside of who she was, to become someone she wanted to be.

Samantha would like to add:

> Drama has given a home to my imagination and a place for my mind to run free; it's where I have always belonged but had never found; this is a feeling that is worth overcoming any mental illness to me.

In drama, we learn how to inhabit another character. If people can channel this skill and use it to create a confident version of themselves, they can practise walking, talking and behaving in positive ways until these become second nature.

Those who suffer from low self-esteem can often go on to develop a mental illness. If people do not understand what motivates other people to behave the way that they do, they can end up believing that everything that happens around them is a reflection of them. People with low self-esteem and mental health issues can often feel guilty for no reason at all. Drama helps them to think about why characters might act the way that they do and understand that human beings are complex and not everything centres around them.

Charlie Brooks, actress and drama teacher, says:

Drama can help with mental illness by themes of inclusion, memory and escapism, and by taking on another character. Self-esteem can be

Chapter 5

promoted by being part of a team, relying on others, progression, and reward from rehearsals to the finished show.

For shy people, drama is one of the few times in their lives where they can step out of the label of being a shy person. They are given permission to scream, and shout, and laugh without fear of judgement. Drama pushes people's boundaries, helping them to realise that they do not have to conform to the label they have been given. It can help them to realise what they are capable of and what they can be.

Most of the plays and television shows that are written are about consequences too. Looking at a human story from the outside, people can identify the ways that the characters might have made different decisions to bring about a more positive outcome. They can then apply this to their own lives, realising that they do have the power to influence what happens around them and, more importantly, to themselves.

On a final note, at the time of writing this, my Samantha is now very close to finishing her Stage and Media degree at Kingston College of Further Education, something three years ago, I would not have thought possible. She has pushed herself in every which way outside of her comfort zone, continually challenging herself – never letting the OCD define or stop her from pursuing her passion.

All of which could not have been achieved without the unconditional first-class teaching, constant care and support from all of Samantha's wonderful tutors – to them I will always be grateful.

Some of Samantha's tutors would like to add to this. Laura McCormack, the course leader, says:

Over the last two years the course team have all watched Samantha grow in confidence and self-belief. She has lovely comic qualities and her eccentricity is charming and watchable; she shows a natural flare for communicating a story to an audience. Sam has been embraced by her year group, in part due to her own warmth and openness, and through this supportive environment she has really come into her own. It is going to be an exciting next few months watching her grow to her fullest.

Blair Kelly, one of Samantha's lecturers, says:

I have worked with Sam since 2015 when she undertook the HNC Performing Arts, and she is now in her final year of the BA Acting for Stage and Media. Sam has continually challenged herself, and there is a marked difference between her confidence in my singing classes on the HNC, to the singing class in BA Year 2, and now again in Professional Practice in BA Year 3 where she is making active contributions to class discussions and challenging other students' statements with authority. Sam has transitioned from the fear of getting everything wrong in her first singing classes with me, to being an empowered actor with confidence and flair.

Carlos Santos, lecturer and course leader, concludes with:

Sam is now defined by her successes, not her challenges; they have become invisible to the naked eye and all we see now is her beauty.

Massage

Massage therapy is a common treatment for the relief of sports injuries, strains and rehabilitation. However, its benefits are more than just physical; it can also be an effective way to relieve anxiety, depression and other mental health issues, as well as help to improve sleep quality. Although life stresses are unavoidable, negative feelings and insomnia can be helped with the positive benefits that massage therapy can offer.

Debbie Pennington, yoga and massage specialist, confirms this:

Touch has extraordinary healing power and it is something massage therapists learn about in training. Caring and compassionate touch is something that over thousands of years has largely declined between humans, especially in the UK. Massage is a valuable therapy that is often misunderstood and considered to be more of an indulgent treat than an aid to our wellbeing. You only need to look at the animal world to see physical interactions that are instinctive and natural, but may be missing in the lives of many people.

Several research projects have shown that touch in general, and massage therapy in particular, are effective in reducing diagnosed and self-reported OCD and anxiety disorders. Some people with issues or phobias around touch may specifically seek out massage as a way to experience positive touch in their lives. The benefits of massage in respect of OCD, as long as the client is accepting of the touch, can be great. These include deep relaxation, regulation of breathing and heart rate, improving sleep, reducing muscle tension arising from nervous tension, calming of the mind through the release of emotional stress, and helping to stem panic attacks and heart-pounding discomfort.

Most OCD sufferers experience a chronic state of anxiety which can build and build, and massage has the capacity to bring those levels down to base again and re-balance the emotions, helping reinforce a parasympathetic [relaxed] state of wellbeing. This is not a cure, but regular massage and breathing techniques can prove to be a lifeline when living with OCD.

Josh, a carer for his girlfriend, champions massage and how it helped him to sleep better:

Finding out my girlfriend suffers from OCD was very difficult for me and caused me many sleepless nights worrying about it. This obviously did not help my ability to support her, so I needed to find something that could help me to sleep. I went for a massage, on recommendation, and have not looked back. I now have regular massages, even just for 30 minutes, and I find this takes away some of my tension and anxiety over my girlfriend's condition. It enables me to relax so much more and also for me to support my girlfriend better.

Reflexology

Reflexology is a complementary therapy that is based on the theory that different areas on the feet correspond with different areas of the body. By working on these areas, it is possible to aid relaxation and improve coping with the stresses that life can bring.

Alison, a hypnotherapist and reflexologist, explains how reflexology can benefit mental health and wellbeing:

Many who experience some form of mental health problem usually suffer from high levels of stress, anxiety, depression and unwanted thoughts, leaving them feeling overwhelmed, exhausted and unable to cope with day-to-day activities. They frequently find themselves in a state of fight, flight or freeze, and unable to break the cycle.

Research in Taiwan suggests that reflexology can have a stimulating effect on the vagus nerve, encouraging the mind and body to return to a calmer state where levels of the stress hormone, adrenalin [or 'epinephrin'] reduce and the body begins to rebalance. This can then help with anxiety and depression, and lifts mood by raising the levels of endorphins that induce feelings of wellbeing and aid sleep.

It is a deeply relaxing treatment and many express the benefits of restored sleep, an increased feeling of wellbeing and a sense of calmness returning, thus helping to break the fight/flight cycle mentioned above. It can also help with digestive stress such as IBS (irritable bowel syndrome), migraines and hormonal imbalances which often accompany mental health issues as signs in the physical body that all is not well.

The theory is that all the systems and organs of the body are mapped out on the feet and known as 'reflexes'. By working each reflex, the body is encouraged to rebalance and restore itself naturally. The spine, for example, is reflected on the inside of the each foot and represents quite a large reflex, thus benefiting from the massage techniques during treatment. In essence, the nervous system benefits and clients usually experience a sense of relaxation.

Acupuncture

Traditional acupuncture is based on ancient principles which go back nearly two thousand years; over this time it has been found to have great benefits for mental and physical health and function. The focus is on the individual and not the illness, therefore two people with the same diagnosis could receive different acupuncture treatments. It is believed, by traditional acupuncturists, that illness and pain arise when the body's *qi*, or vital energy, is unable to flow freely – therefore, the overall objective of acupuncture treatment is to restore the body's balance.

Angela, traditional Chinese medicine (TCM) acupuncturist and sports therapist, tells us more about these benefits:

There is limited literature written about acupuncture or Chinese medicine for the treatment specifically of OCD. However, there are books about how acupuncture, Chinese medicine, Qi Gong and acupressure can help with mental-emotional wellbeing, including alleviating anxiety and stress, of which OCD is a part. As yet, there is also relatively little research on acupuncture for general anxiety disorders, including OCD, but what is out there seems to be leading to positive outcomes in the use of acupuncture for mental health. It has shown that acupuncture can promote relaxation by activating the parasympathetic nervous system and it can lead to positive mood changes by regulating the body's neurotransmitters and hormones (such as GABA, serotonin and dopamine).

Traditional Chinese medicine (TCM) has been used for thousands of years as a main medicine to treat a variety of conditions. It works by restoring balance to the body's energy system, or Qi. It is based on the belief that Qi flows along meridians, or energy channels, all over the body, linked to our internal organs, and when there is imbalance, such as Qi or blood stagnation, or Qi or blood deficiency, or an imbalance of the yin and yang energies of the body, it gives rise to various pathologies. However, unlike the approach of Western medicine, which is more of a 'one size fits all', TCM takes a more holistic approach. The body and mind are very much interconnected. Emotions when out of balance can affect our internal organs, but also an imbalance of the energy in our internal organs can influence our emotions. More specifically, TCM believes that each organ is influenced by specific emotions: anger affects the liver, joy affects the heart, sadness affects the lungs and heart, worry affects the lungs and spleen, fear affects the kidneys, shock affects the heart. Examples of the physical effects of an emotional disharmony are: fear, which affects the kidneys, when out of control may cause symptoms such as diarrhoea, incontinence, palpitations, insomnia and night sweating; pensiveness, or constant thinking and brooding, affects the spleen and it can cause the Qi to knot, with symptoms such as poor appetite, tiredness and abdominal bloating.

A TCM practitioner, during a treatment, besides using acupuncture may also use other techniques such as cupping, moxa [or 'moxibustion'] and/or herbal medicine and, most importantly, will give dietary and lifestyle recommendations, together possibly with bodywork and/or breathing exercises *(such as meditation techniques and Qi Gong), all tailored to the patient's individual needs.*

From personal experience, clients overall report an enhanced feeling of wellbeing and relaxation following an acupuncture treatment. This, in itself, leads to reduced stress and anxiety, increased positive thinking and, together with other treatments, it can help towards the healing journey.

Steve champions traditional acupuncture and the positive effect it has had on his overall wellbeing:

> As with any sort of 'therapy', you do indeed receive the more you give. Traditional acupuncture is no exception. Unlike its Western counterparts, this time-honoured process of balancing the spiritual with the physical – focuses on energy or Chi. It may not be for everybody, but this incredible 'preventative medicine' has saved my life and has done so many times during the last three decades. It's also about trust, and the relationship between practitioner and patient. I have been so lucky to have had the help of just three good people through the years – and all from the same 'school of thought'! As a communicator, I am blessed that I have been able to express my feelings, and have been rewarded in kind. But even if you are not as outgoing as some – and if you have tried the Western way of medication and temporary results – do have a think about traditional acupuncture. Even if you give a little ... that return may just be getting to the root of the problem. Whatever it takes... to make a difference.

The willingness of a sufferer to engage with alternative therapies shows that they are seeking positivity and a way to combat and conquer their illness. This is one of the most crucial and valuable steps towards recovery.

For the carer, alternative treatments can provide respite in the form of 'time-out' to help renew their strength, emotionally and physically, and to enable them to face the challenges that they deal with in their role as a carer for someone suffering from OCD.

I cannot reiterate enough the point that everyone is different, and if one therapy does not work for you or the sufferer, be open minded and not afraid to try another. This chapter has provided only a brief description of each therapy. Contact details of the therapists mentioned are provided in the Resources section at the back of the book (page 184).

Chapter 6

OCD and other mental illnesses

Astonishingly and sadly, around one in four people in Britain will experience some form of mental illness in their lifetime, ranging from the more common and well-known issues, such as depression, anxiety, OCD, eating disorders and self-harm, to rarer, lesser known ones, such as schizophrenia and personality disorders. It is important to remember that this figure is only based on the registered sufferers actively seeking medical help. I am sure there must be countless others who are suffering in silence, both in the UK and internationally, adding to these ever-increasing numbers.

My personal and professional findings, more recently confirmed by a survey I prepared in which numerous people kindly participated via my social media channels, support the suggestion that OCD may be directly interconnected with other mental illnesses, such as depression, self-harm and eating disorders. A staggering 85 per cent of sufferers surveyed had at least one other mental health issue in addition to their OCD. The results of this survey highlight how OCD can co-exist alongside other mental illnesses.

Aimee shares her frustrations from her own experience:

Mental illnesses cannot be separated into a neat little box and treated separately – often they entwine and feed off each other. My local NHS funding body only allows one referral for mental illness at a time – you cannot be treated for more than one simultaneously. This is a very dated and simplistic approach. It is mainly dictated by money and rules of funding, rather than by the needs of the patient.

Sue, Lucy's mother, says of her daughter's experience:

From the start of her illness, the psychiatrists were wondering what had come first: the depression or the anorexia; and therefore, what should they treat. In many cases, treating anorexia and re-feeding the brain lifts the depression and people start to make a recovery. However, in Lucy's case, after two years of treatment for an eating disorder, the NHS services decided that transferring focus to the depression would facilitate recovery of the eating disorder. Unfortunately, transferring focus enabled the eating disorder to gain strength again and eating became more of a problem at a faster speed than the counselling and medication for depression could help her.

Three years on, we have made a different connection. Lucy's problems all started with obsessive behaviours: constantly cooking, watching the same TV programme over and over, a need to do a certain amount of exercise every day, controlling food etc. She is also a Strep B bacteria carrier and occasionally suffers from Strep B throat infections, needing treatment with antibiotics. I mention this as we have now discovered a link between Strep B and OCD behaviour. Now instead of treating the eating disorder or the depression, we are tackling the OCD behaviour; breaking down Lucy's habits and trying to help her stop her obsessive behaviours, which rule her life. We realise why perhaps the antidepressants haven't ever fully worked – they won't cure OCD.

To help you understand the possible links and connections I will endeavour to explain the more common mental health issues in greater detail in this chapter, together with the indicators when interlinked with OCD.

Like OCD, all mental health issues can affect anyone irrespective of their age, gender, sexuality, ethnicity or social background. The effect on each individual can vary, as can the length of time a person suffers from a particular problem; these mental health issues can be defined as conditions that influence a person's way of thinking, feeling, behaviour and/or all three. Individuals who have milder symptoms of mental illness may not appear visibly ill in a physical sense to the outside world, but the distress and difficulty in mental functionality on the inside can cause great fear and anxiety. These vivid thoughts and internal feelings can become stronger and much more problematic if left undetected and untreated, and the sufferer will be ill equipped to tackle this alone. If the symptoms are more severe, there may be more obvious external signs. Either way, mental illness is just as serious as any physical condition and deserves the same level of attention, respect and intervention, yet, sadly, it is often misunderstood and dismissed because of the lack of visible evidence to the human eye. It is important to remember that it is the most natural thing in the world to feel happy and uplifted when something positive happens in our lives, as it is to feel sad, anxious, fearful or angry when something negative or worrying occurs. My mum once pointed out to me that bad days are essential in life if we are to recognise and appreciate the good days. Part of ensuring good mental health and wellbeing is the ability to recognise the difference between natural emotions and prolonged unnatural ones, possibly indicating a potential issue.

As with OCD, other mental illnesses can be kept secret by the sufferer, who will at times feel embarrassed, ashamed and lonely, but because it is often hidden it is difficult to quantify the actual extent of mental illness. Personally, I would be inclined to measure the severity by looking at the impact of a condition on the life of the person experiencing the illness, and those of the people around them.

Questions you could ask yourself are:

- Can the person concentrate in school?
- Can the person hold down a job?

- Can the person socialise?
- Can the person maintain friendships or romantic relationships?
- Can the person sleep at night?
- Is the person looking after his/her body and physical health?
- Is the person's unusual behaviour causing disruption within the family or home environment?

All of these factors can be negatively affected by mental illness on quite a significant scale.

Before I begin to describe some of the signs and symptoms, I would like to reiterate that this is only a general and fairly basic guide; everyone who experiences mental illness does so in different and diverse ways, making it impossible to encompass each and every sufferer's experience. Parents, friends, partners and carers who regularly spend time with their loved ones will know them better than anyone else, but hopefully the information below will help to determine when the line is crossed between common-or-garden angst as opposed to something deeper and potentially more sinister. At the risk of repeating myself too many times, there is no substitute for intuition, so if you feel that something is amiss then there's probably good reason for further exploration.

In my experience, there are five main types of common mental illness. OCD is one of them, with the remaining four being anxiety, depression, eating disorders and self-harm. I describe how they may present themselves below. Although each has its own distinctive characteristic symptoms, they are often intertwined and with overlapping features.

Anxiety

Anxiety can be a stand-alone condition in the form known as 'generalised anxiety disorder' (GAD). It can also be the starting point for many other mental illnesses. It is the most common form of mental illness in the Western world and can be the glue that holds all the others together, perpetuating the cycle where other conditions are involved: it is both the cause *and* the effect.

'Anxiety' is a general term for a variety of disorders that cause nervousness, fear, apprehension, paranoia and worry. Life can be full of stressful situations and most of us live with a heightened sense of unease accompanied by a moderate level of anxiety, due to the unsettling world we live in today; it is our nervous system's normal response to a perceived threat or danger. However, when this feeling gathers momentum and the sufferer finds it impossible to control, it can become a mental illness and be physically and emotionally debilitating.

Mental and physical symptoms of anxiety vary widely, but the person may experience:

- feelings of panic, fear, paranoia, insanity and uneasiness
- repeated thoughts or flashbacks of traumatic experiences
- disrupted sleep, nightmares and/or an inability to get to sleep altogether
- cold, sweaty, numbness or tingling in the hands and/or feet
- shortness of breath, rapid or irregular breathing or palpitations
- bouts of dizziness, nausea and possibly a dry mouth
- the need to avoid certain places or items.

Children are growing up faster than ever before, and as parents or carers it can be hard for us to appreciate just how difficult they may be finding it, coping with the pressures of school and friendship as well as their feelings and ever-changing hormone levels as they mature. Their interaction with social media and the internet is often an attempt to understand the world, and can cause its own problems. Anxiety can be specifically an issue for the younger generation as they are not always able to verbalise or convey how they are feeling, let alone understand it. Listening to many of my clients aged from eight upwards, I often hear that their anxiety is heightened after spending time on social media sites or reading magazines, watching internet channels or reality TV shows, to the point that some even have to remove themselves to avoid the constant barrage of mixed messages and confusion. All of these can give a false perception of how they think their life should be, and media influences such as these can make the sufferer feel inadequate, insignificant, excluded and invisible.

Molly tells us of her experience with anxiety and social media:

The darker side of social media is something that I am passionate to get across to younger people. Social media platforms such as Instagram are great ways for businesses and people to get noticed; however, they also bring a lot of pressure, especially for younger people. I received my first iPhone at the age of 16, and just a week after receiving it I was introduced to Instagram by a friend. Now aged 21 I now have just under 1000 followers and until a few months ago posted regularly (almost every week). Each photo posted had at least 20 different takes, followed by finding the perfect filter. I would get compliments from people at work and younger girls about how cool and fun my Instagram profile looked. It wasn't until a few months ago I realised that everything on Instagram is all for show and in fact not at all real. Young people are now getting iPhones from the ages of 12 or less and its scary to think that they will be exposed to these posts of happy, healthy, successful people wondering why they don't look like that or have a life like that. If I felt pressure at 16 and didn't realise until 21 that it is all a show, I fear for our future generations who will be exposed to these images even younger, as they can have a huge effect on their self-esteem.

Hannah, a teacher, explores the impact social media has on her students:

> Every year I get a new class of children and every year the percentage of children who suffer from anxieties at some level rises. Whether it be worry about friendship groups, work load, home life or organisation, the children struggle more and more to maintain a healthy mind. I would say that I spend about an hour each week trying to reassure and support children with their anxieties to ensure that their time in school is as stress-free and calm as possible. It worries me that this will continue to rise each year, unless there is more support for children with anxieties.

Anxiety is by no means exclusive to children; it also affects many adults in their everyday life. It is estimated that approximately 25 per cent of adults suffer from anxiety at some point in their life. These figures do not come as a surprise, bearing in mind the ever-increasing pace of life, combined with the pressures of everyday living.

Lisa, a mother of three children and with a part-time job, explains how her busy life has caused her to suffer from anxiety and mild OCD:

> A few years ago I was a full-time mum, but due to financial pressures I have had to get a part-time job. I have found that since then, I have become more and more anxious, trying to be the 'perfect' wife and mother, making sure my children get to go to every club, party, school event and so on, whilst making sure dinner is on the table every night and the house is spotless. I am not ashamed to say that this stress and anxiety have had quite an impact on my everyday mental wellbeing. I have developed a mild form of OCD around time keeping, organisation and obsessing over being perfect; often, I feel something bad might happen if things are not in perfect order at home and in the family.

A highly anxious person may develop some form of coping mechanism to help combat the overbearing anxiety which then leads into another form of mental illness, stealthily linking them together, with anxiety being the common denominator (cause/effect) in nearly all mental illnesses.

A significant proportion of those with OCD also have GAD or another form of anxiety disorder; these two conditions are often interlinked because they can feed off and fuel each other. The comorbid (concurrent) anxiety disorder can be due to worry and dread of an attack of obsessive thoughts and compulsions that the sufferer knows is imminent.

Dominic tells us of his anxiety and OCD:

> My constant worry and dread over the content of the thoughts I get have caused my anxiety to sky rocket. I am constantly living in fear of what my mind is going to come up with next. The OCD and anxiety go hand in hand for me, one triggering the other, like a vicious circle.

Depression

Depression is a common condition that can cause lengthy periods of low mood, a lack of interest in the things that the sufferer used to find enjoyable, feelings of guilt and low self-worth, disturbance in sleep patterns, loss of appetite, loss of energy and/or compromised concentration. Depression is very different from just feeling fed up, a bit sad or down in the dumps, which we all feel from time to time, usually due to something specific that affects us on a personal level. A person suffering from depression will experience these feelings too, but in addition to this they suffer from the permanent weight of extreme anxiety, negativity, hopelessness and despair. These feelings do not subside but stay with the sufferer every hour of every day like the darkest of clouds, overshadowing everything they try to do.

There are thought to be two types of depression: reactive depression and organic depression. The difference between the two is that organic depression comes from within the sufferer for no apparent or specific reason, unrelated to the external features and circumstances of their life, while reactive depression is the complete opposite, being a rational response to life events such as the death of a loved one or the breakdown of a relationship, redundancy or diagnosis of a terminal illness. Reactive depression can pass when the person becomes acclimatised and adjusts to the emotional trigger.

People who suffer from depression are often unaware that they are in the grip of it unless it is pointed out to them by someone who knows them well enough to recognise the symptoms. As with some other mental illnesses, this condition can distort their perceptions of what is and is not normal for them. It is often borne out of low self-esteem, anxiety or another mental illness, but it can equally be their root cause.

By its very nature, organic depression is not a logical response to the things a sufferer has in their life: it does not take into account a person's luxuries, possessions, circle of friends, social life or income; it can strike anyone indiscriminately at any time. Many successful, popular, wealthy professionals who appear to have 'everything', with the world at their feet, can battle inwardly with depression.

My dear friend Bobby Davro talks of his struggles:

> To the outside world, I am a successful, confident, funny entertainer. However, what would surprise many people is that at some of the highest points of my career, I have suffered from dark times, depression, low self-esteem and a feeling of worthlessness. It is in my experience that antidepressant medication and the like are prescribed too easily, leaving the patient unaware of an alternative therapy that in the long term can be a much better alternative to improve their mental health.

Roughly 50 per cent of depression sufferers, once recovered, may never experience it again in their lifetime, but sadly for the remainder there can be unpredictable recurrences throughout the years which can make things incredibly difficult for them and their families.

Typical symptoms of depression may include the following. The person may:

- sleep a lot or experience insomnia
- feel very sluggish or be overly fidgety
- have trouble focusing for any amount of time and experience a lack of motivation
- experience a continuous low mood or sadness and could feel irritable and intolerant of others
- experience a lack of enjoyment in previously enjoyable activities
- start to feel anxious or worried and experience low self-esteem
- have feelings of worthlessness and hopelessness
- have difficulty in making decisions
- experience suicidal thoughts or thoughts of harming others
- experience feelings of guilt and suffer from tearfulness
- have thoughts of death.

Typical physical symptoms of depression may include the following. The person may:

- experience a change in appetite, and weight loss or weight gain
- experience lack of energy and/or slowed movement or speech
- experience changes to the menstrual cycle (in women)
- have unexplained aches and pains.

Typical social symptoms of depression include the following. The person may:

- have reduced contact with friends
- have less interest in hobbies and activities
- have decreased performance at school or work
- have difficulties in home and family life
- stop taking part in social activities.

Again, from personal experience, I would say the most important thing to look for is a change in a person's demeanour. If for example a teenager continually says, 'I hate the world', but then regularly goes out to meet with their friends in the park or goes to play a ball game or takes part in other fun activities in contrast to the words they mutter, then the chances are they are probably not depressed. If a loved one or friend constantly complains about how much they hate their job or asks, 'What is the point?' yet goes to play golf, or socialises regularly, having fun and living in the moment without being constantly preoccupied, then the chances are they are probably not suffering from depression either. However, please remember prolonged apathy and constant negativity are the building blocks of depression. If the person is constantly feeling that everyone else's life is somehow better than theirs, and what is the point of their life, and what are they doing with it, then there could be a need for help and medical intervention.

For some, the restraints and control that the continuous cycle of OCD rituals bring can contribute to the onset of depression. Research[9] suggests people with OCD generally have one major depressive episode at some point in their lives which generally occurs after the OCD symptoms have begun, as a result of the continual distress caused by those symptoms.

Natasha says:

> Depression goes hand in hand with my OCD; it makes it so incredibly hard to fight and cope.

Eating disorders

Generally, eating disorders are defined as a distorted pattern of thinking about food and everything associated with it. They involve the sufferer abusing food, exercise and their own bodies to dangerous levels, however the problem originated, and are characterised by disordered thinking and mental distress. Like self-harming, they are an indication that something is happening in the brain, with the effects on the body being the visible symptoms. Eating disorders can be measured not by a set of weighing scales, but by an assessment of feelings, thoughts and behaviours.

Interestingly, eating disorders frequently coexist with other mental illnesses. They have been linked to alcoholism and drug addiction, and have strong links with OCD, anxiety, self-harm and depression.

There are many types of eating disorders and within these types there are literally hundreds of variations and symptoms unique to the sufferer, but the condition usually begins with simply eating too little or too much, and the obsession with eating, exercise and body image follows, leading to strict, tailored changes in the diet, behaviour and lifestyle of the sufferer.

With so many variations in dietary preferences in today's society, such as veganism and vegetarianism, and gluten and other food intolerances, it is becoming more difficult to define 'normal' eating. For the majority of people, however, food and calorie intake/expenditure do not preoccupy their thinking and their lives. An eating disorder is an illness that permeates all aspects of the sufferer's life from the minute they wake up to the minute they go to bed; some even dream about food when they sleep so that it dominates their lives 24/7. It is a serious health condition that can be both physically and emotionally destructive.

The three most well-known forms of eating disorder are: anorexia nervosa, bulimia nervosa, and compulsive and binge eating disorder. They are described in brief below, yet the most common actual diagnosis is OSFED ('other specified feeding or eating disorder'), which means that the sufferer does not completely fit with the official criteria for any one eating disorder in particular.

Chapter 6

Anorexia nervosa

The official definition of anorexia nervosa is 'self-imposed starvation'. However, anorexia nervosa is not really about how little a person eats; it is about their desire to control what they eat. The sufferer will generally know exactly how much they eat in a day, at what times and how many calories they consume. They will often weigh and measure their food and are likely to become fearful in situations where they have to deviate from the food plan they have set for themselves.

The sufferer will go to great lengths to eat according to the rules their illness tells them are necessary. They will often hide their behaviour, lie to their loved ones and engage in morally questionable behaviours which prioritise their condition above anything and anyone else in their lives.

Signs of anorexia nervosa which help distinguish it from a diet or phase are below. It is important to note that usually there will be more than one sign, although that is not always the case. The person may:

- avoid food and meal times
- make excuses to avoid eating, such as having 'eaten earlier'
- carefully weigh and portion food
- use continual self-effacing language, such as repeatedly claiming to be 'fat'
- check calories and the fat content of food
- keep lists of food consumed
- deny hunger
- continually look for approval and validation
- hide food that they have led others to believe had been eaten
- pick out a few specific foods and eat these in very small quantities
- start doing intense and/or compulsive exercise.

With the physical signs of anorexia nervosa, the person may:

- have a rapid weight loss
- have hair loss on the scalp
- experience dizzy spells/feel faint
- experience constipation and stomach pain
- develop 'lanugo' – soft, downy hair on the face and body
- experience poor circulation and feel cold (particularly in the hands, nose and feet)
- experience dry, rough or discoloured skin
- experience dehydration.
- in girls, periods may stop or not start in the first place.

The physical symptoms above usually clear up once the sufferer enters into recovery; however, it is important to note that they are at risk of long-term health consequences, such as osteoporosis and infertility.

Bulimia nervosa

Bulimia nervosa can be just as serious as anorexia nervosa and yet is more difficult to detect from the outside, since sufferers are quite often a 'normal' weight, or even slightly overweight.

People who have bulimia nervosa continually 'binge' eat large quantities of food in a short period of time and then 'purge', finding ways to rid their body of the food consumed, most commonly by vomiting. Sufferers of anorexia nervosa can also 'purge', but it is the consumption of large quantities of food that is the defining factor that distinguishes bulimia nervosa – that and there being no loss of weight.

Some signs of bulimia nervosa may include the following. The person may:

- experience urges to eat large amounts of food
- experience mood swings
- experience anxiety and/or depression
- start to vomit after eating

- start acting secretly and be reluctant to socialise.

Effects of bulimia nervosa on the body may include the following. The person may:
- experience a sore throat and/or bad breath
- start using laxatives
- engage in compulsive exercise
- experience dry or patchy skin
- constantly put themselves down
- have feelings of shame or guilt
- experience irregular periods (in girls)
- experience tiredness
- experience redness around the knuckles
- experience puffiness of the face and fingers.

Compulsive and binge eating

Compulsive and binge eating has only been recognised as an official eating disorder fairly recently, which is an important step forward. When people overeat we do not tend to have as much sympathy for them as those who starve themselves, even though the effects on the body and mind can be just as harmful and the underlying emotions just as distressing.

People who have this condition suffer from episodes of uncontrolled eating, followed by guilt and depression, although they do not then purge. In addition to eating large quantities of food, the sufferer will also usually have a 'frenzied' feeling as though they are unable to control their actions. They may continue to eat long after they have become full.

Some signs of binge/compulsive eating include the following. The person may:
- have a fear of not being able to control eating and/or not being able to stop eating
- have a fear of eating around others

- experience fatigue
- sporadically use popular diet plans
- hide food in secret places to eat later
- have secretive eating patterns.

Effects of binge/compulsive eating on the body may include the following. The person may:
- experience weight gain
- believe that life would be better if they were able to lose weight
- put themselves down, especially after eating
- become out of breath after light activity
- experience excessive sweating
- blame personal failures in social and professional life on their weight
- experience depression/mood swings
- suffer from high blood pressure and/or cholesterol
- experience leg and joint pain
- experience decreased mobility owing to weight gain
- experience loss of sexual desire
- experience insomnia
- experience poor sleeping habits.

It is important to note here that it is possible to binge eat or eat compulsively and not be overweight. However, this is still a problem, both physically and mentally. Our health is dictated not by how much we weigh, but by how much fat is around our internal organs. It is possible to be a small size and have unseen fat around the heart and arteries. Using food as a kind of drug is also not healthy emotionally. There is a difference between this and simply having a 'high metabolism' or 'large appetite'.

Other recognised eating disorders include **orthorexia** (sufferers become obsessed with healthy eating to the extent that it totally dominates their lives), **body dysmorphia** (sufferers become fixated with the idea that aspects of their own appearance are extremely flawed and go to extraordinary measures to hide or fix them), **compulsive exercising** and **bigorexia** (gym culture, especially among boys). Of these, orthorexia and bigorexia are relatively new and becoming more widely recognised via the media and charities, raising awareness of mental health issues as their incidence continues to rise.

As an eating disorder manifests within a person it becomes stronger and stronger, controlling them despite their believing the opposite – that they are in fact in control – which can lead to obsessional behaviour.

Eating disorders and OCD can develop hand in hand alongside each other, and in today's society where we are much more aware of the impact of certain foods on our health and wellbeing, food phobias are becoming very common in children and young adults. Allergic reactions, choking, being sick or being poisoned are the most feared.

Children in particular can be quickly affected by words innocently used in association with food from a very young age as they are very impressionable and can listen in with selective hearing to conversations that may be jokey or otherwise. Words used in general, everyday conversations can be picked up and a child's imagination play upon them, leading to fear of certain foods and triggering rituals and ways to avoid the situations they have heard being talked about. Over time this can create obsessive thinking patterns and behaviour, so potentially causing the onset of OCD.

For instance:

- 'Do not eat that burger or you could get mad cow disease!'
- 'Do not eat boiled sweets, you could choke to death!'
- 'Do not eat that piece of cake, you could get fat!'
- 'Only eat organic foods or you could get cancer!'

The connection between OCD and eating disorders can be so close that often the parallels can become too blurred to separate the two. Statistically, people with eating disorders have a higher rate of OCD than the rest of the population, and vice versa, so diagnosis and separation of the two conditions often remains indistinct due to their striking similarities. The difficulty lies in recognising whether the condition is:

- Food-related OCD – a fear of food contamination / only magical numbers of mouthfuls of food allowed per mealtime / only certain coloured foods allowed / restricted food groups – all of which may bring about food limitations thus leading to weight loss; or
- an entirely separate eating disorder characterised by abnormal or disturbed thinking and eating patterns.

Whether dieting and exercising excessively with anorexia nervosa or bingeing and purging with bulimia nervosa, both behaviours characteristically stem from intrusive obsessive thoughts based on body image, perfectionism and social approval. In both cases, the incessant food and body fixations lead to anxiety levels spiking that can only be reduced by ritualistic compulsions, such as cutting and weighing food or compulsively purging to relieve the obsessive guilt and shame following binges, or in some cases just eating. The common denominator and unquestionable link between OCD and eating disorders is the engulfing presence of obsessions and compulsions and the feeling of never being 'just right'.

David, who is recovering from an eating disorder and OCD, tells us of his struggles:

I am now in recovery from anorexia and OCD; it has been very challenging for me as these two mental illnesses seem to have a strong hold together. During most of my illness I felt compelled to eat at specific times; however, because of my eating disorder, sometimes the timings would not work out and I could miss almost all my meals in one day. My life was completely dominated by it. I have been having therapy for the past 12 months, and part of that has made me challenge the timings of my eating when I can. I am now on the road to recovery, but I still have a long way to go.

As OCD sufferers will repeatedly check locked doors and windows even though they know they are locked, a sufferer from anorexia nervosa, who knows they are thin, will continue to feel compelled to lose weight despite the image they see in the mirror, as they will think they are just not thin enough, and the sufferer from bulimia nervosa will persist with their binge/purge cycle and a compulsive eater with the amount of food they consume, as it will never seem to be enough.

As awareness and public consciousness grow and the stigma begins to slowly reduce, more and more people are recognising the signs in themselves and are becoming willing to admit that they are sufferers. Being able to reach out for help without fear of being labelled 'crazy' or being at risk of damaging their future opportunities in relationships, workplace and life in general is paramount to their recovery.

Aimee talks of how her OCD and eating disorder are interlinked:

For the past 10 years, OCD has been very closely linked to my eating disorder in many ways. I have many rules, routines and rituals regarding what I eat, how, why, when, and who with. I developed these to minimise the chance of my overeating or bingeing. My OCD now fuels the eating disorder itself. I am aware that these rules are self-imposed, but I cannot bring myself to stop them. They have become my safety mechanism to ensure nothing bad happens and therefore it feels counter-intuitive to let them go.

Self-harm

Self-harm means exactly what it says – it occurs when a person chooses to inflict physical harm on their body. It varies from person to person, but is usually a way of indirectly dealing with difficult or complicated issues in a sufferer's life and is often inflicted by means of cutting or burning the skin. It can also involve a sufferer putting their safety in jeopardy by voluntarily being in hazardous situations or exercising to the point of pain.

The mental health charity Mind defines self-harm as 'a way of expressing very deep distress'. Often people do not know why they self-harm. Though many sufferers go to great lengths to hide what they are doing, it can be a means of communicating what cannot be put into words or even into thoughts, and has been described as an inner scream.

Eating disorders can also be described as a form of self-harm due to the physical damage inflicted on the body in order to block out what is happening in the mind. As with other mental illnesses, including as OCD, self-harm is inflicted to bring relief to the sufferer, albeit only temporarily, so the cycle repeats and repeats with the behaviours becoming both physically and mentally addictive and, in some cases, more severe.

According to the Mental Health Foundation, the UK has the highest incidence of any European country for self-harm; it is thought to affect 400 in every 100,000 (that's one in 250) of the population – males and females equally. The figure is likely to be much higher, however, as many people who self-harm do so in secret and seldom tell anyone. Although anybody can be affected, the majority are between the ages of 11 and 25 years old. Higher rates of self-harm are evident in people already suffering from borderline personality disorders, depression and eating disorders.

Self-harming can include scratching, pinching, hitting or cutting different parts of the body, hair-pulling, burning, or anything which is done deliberately to cause pain, including less obvious forms such as risk-taking, drug overdose or simply not taking care of the person's own physical or emotional needs.

In children, harming wild animals, pets or younger siblings can also be a sign of internal anxiety which if left undiagnosed could then lead to other mental health issues, such as eating disorders, depression and OCD.

Many young people who self-harm say that it enables them to feel something, rather than the numbness which can be associated with depression or other mental illnesses. Whilst teenage girls often use self-harm as a physical expression of familiar yet painful emotions, teenage boys are likely to self-harm because they do not have the emotional vocabulary to express how they feel. While generally done in secret, self-harm can be a way of attention seeking, physicalising an internal pain for an outside world to see in a way that demands interaction. It can also be an indicator of suicidal thoughts, allowing the self-harmer to test the water without actually attempting the real thing. It is often described as a pressure cooker of emotions that build up on the inside and self-harming is a way of releasing that pressure. It can be linked to feelings of self-loathing, unworthiness and low self-esteem.

The symptoms of self-harm can be very hard to spot in young people, because they will very often conceal them from their parents, teachers and friends. At the same time, self-harm has recently been noted to be 'contagious' in schools whereby students will emulate each other's inflictions, so it is a good idea to ensure that all friends connected to the self-harmer know that intervention is taking place, giving a strong and clear message that it is a very serious issue and not to be mimicked.

Self-harmers young and old will usually cut parts of their body – arms or upper legs, most commonly – which can be hidden under clothing. However, you know your loved one, and you will recognise any change in their behaviour which could indicate self-harm; this could include unexplained bruises, hair loss or bald patches, scars, wearing long sleeves or long trousers even in hot weather, and generally spending a lot of time alone. Some of the signs of self-harm are explained as 'accidental', with the self-harmer making excuses for the bruises or the scars, so the most important factor to consider here is the frequency with which they appear and the persistence of injury. Some of the physical signs to look out for are as follows. The person may:

- have unexplained bruises on parts of their body
- have cigarette burns on parts of their body
- have cuts on parts of their body
- have excessive hair loss/unexplained hairless patches on the scalp
- exercise obsessively (more than what is recommended per day)
- keep covered with layers of clothing, especially long sleeves, particularly in hotter weather
- stop taking part in a sport, such as swimming, that means others can see their skin
- experience low mood/tearfulness/lack of motivation or interest
- show changes in eating habits or being secretive about eating – including rapid weight loss or gain
- experience alcohol or drug misuse.

Self-harming has entered a very dangerous era by way of the internet, where sufferers, once perceived to be secretive and ashamed of their self-inflictions, covering up to hide their scars or abrasions, are now joining online communities and sharing with other self-harmers their scars like 'badges of honour', their painful and misplaced pledge of allegiance to a very disturbing worldwide club.

Self-harming can be a visible indicator of a much deeper and more dangerous emotional issue that requires urgent intervention.

I am often asked the question why some OCD sufferers self-harm. Sometimes, if they fail to carry out compulsive rituals in the 'correct' way, or if they have enjoyed themselves but do not feel worthy of the feeling of happiness, or have achieved a positive goal in life, it can cause such an overwhelming feeling of worthlessness, distress and anxiety that the sufferer may use self-harm as a way to release their inner frustrations. This is known as 'compulsive self-injury'. Common forms of compulsive self-injury include hitting, cutting, biting and burning. The injuries created can range from minor scratches to wounds that need medical attention.

Lucy tells us of her own experience of OCD and self-harm:

The first time I self-harmed I was not in a good way and thought that no-one would take me seriously at any mental health service unless I self-harmed. Originally, I didn't understand the hype or the excitement of it and couldn't understand how anyone could bring themselves to harm themselves in any way. It wasn't until I was deep in my eating disorder and seeing services that I realised why people did it. At first it was to punish myself for eating or to get some relief; it became 'food = self-harm' and it was a routine I got into, and the OCD around it kept growing. It became such a relief to do it and know no-one would see, and I would get away with it and no-one would know. The obsession kept growing to the point where it was uncontrollable and the relief I needed got bigger and bigger and the buzz I would get from it needed to get bigger and bigger. I began getting more extreme in order to try and find some peace in my head, which wasn't going to be found through self-harm, but it was the only thing I felt I had control over, and yet I didn't have any control over it as the OCD was so strong. I would love the feeling and the look and no matter how much people told me it would scar, and I wouldn't want the scars in the future, I didn't care; it was what I wanted at the time. Eventually I began to let go and the more I let go, the easier it began to stop, and the less hold it had over me.

I hope that reading this chapter has given you a better understanding of the more well-known and talked-about mental illnesses, in turn highlighting and demonstrating the possible inter-connective and complex nature of mental illness as a whole. Very rarely do symptoms fall into one neat category, so for the majority it is hard to distinguish one from the other. However, again I cannot emphasise enough the importance of following your instincts and arming yourself with as much applicable knowledge as possible to help you and your loved one find the right recovery path together, remembering always that recovery is possible and sustainable, provided the sufferer really wants it.

Chapter 7

OCD and relationships

Modern everyday life can be overwhelmingly stressful. Every generation has more than likely said the same thing, but that does not make it any less true of the 21st century. Today, the expectations of what family and personal life should be like have been completely transformed compared with even 30 or 40 years ago.

The planet is forever changing, technology advancing, and the population expanding. We undoubtedly have more freedom of choice and are less confined to the traditional gender roles than previous generations. Whilst these advances may seem inevitable, and are generally to be embraced, within relationships some of the realities of contemporary culture have proved to be inadvertently damaging.

Technology

The introduction of smartphones, apps and the internet into our everyday lives, homes, workplaces and schools has given us interconnectedness at all times that could not have been imagined a generation ago. Whilst these devices and systems can provide powerful and positive information and support, they are also a strong indication of our global citizenship as we are constantly distracted and stimulated by the easily accessible outside world that forever circles around us, leaving us little time to think, reflect or even just stand still. The art of talking to each other – and of face-to-face communication – seems to have fallen victim to technology.

Diet

Our relationships are challenged by the way we live. Aside from technology, another contributory factor is the increase in our consumption of convenience foods. Several studies[10] have found that, in the Western world, some mental health issues are clearly linked to a rise in 'junk food' intake and a lack of essential fatty acids, vitamins and minerals. Not only does 'junk food' lack many of the nutrients essential for the brain to function healthily, but it actually includes many components that can have a negative impact on mental health; these components include sugar, caffeine, hydrogenated fats, refined carbs and artificial additives, such as MSG and aspartame. Scientific research linking poor diet to mental health problems is gathering momentum, supporting the contention that an increase in the consumption of convenience foods may be making us jittery, irritable and at times unstable as a result of the chemicals they contain. It can be very difficult, especially when suffering from a mental health issue, to take better care over what we eat, but it really is an essential part of positive mental health care and general wellbeing (see page 90).

Competition and acquisitiveness

The continual pressure to 'keep up with the Joneses' seems to be stronger than it ever was, due in part to the heavy usage of image-focused social media platforms, which can add to already existing feelings of low self-worth, insecurity and financial strain. Now it is all too easy to know how much further ahead the Joneses are – or appear to be! Constantly comparing ourselves to others can affect our personal lives in a very negative way and often we forget the extreme lengths that some people on social media go to, to display their perceived most-perfect version of themselves and their lives. For some people, gaining validation and 'likes' from their followers on social media platforms takes precedence over living in the moment, so the pressure to look a certain way, or be doing the right thing with the 'right people', can be overwhelming. It is healthy to keep in mind that a lot of what we see is artificial perfection.

Globalisation

With our worries about living in a world seemingly full of conflict, terrorism and the threat of climate change, it is no surprise that cracks are starting to appear ever earlier in the mental wellbeing of young people. The weight on their young shoulders is almost too heavy to bear as they face the task of overcoming critical global issues that are constantly evolving. Of course, the pressure does not just apply to the younger generation, but to the population as a whole.

As with every single one of these elements, we cannot control the challenges and misfortunes that come our way, but we can control how we deal with them and how we allow them to affect our relationships with those around us. Everything is okay in moderation. We do not have to allow ourselves to be glued to our devices 24/7; we do not have to allow ourselves to make the wrong dietary choices for our brain's wellbeing and balance; we do not have to allow ourselves to be made to feel inadequate by the riches of others; and whilst we would like a better future for our planet, we need to try to understand that a global effort is needed; the weight of the world cannot be borne on one person's shoulders.

How we navigate our lives significantly affects how we manage our relationships with others; within a family/

partnership, it is quite normal to have fraught and challenging times, as individuals – all with different personalities and needs – jostle to find their own voices and be heard, all together under one roof, even without having someone with OCD, or indeed any mental illness, thrown into the mix.

Living and coping with the dreadful effects of a loved one who has OCD can put an enormous strain on personal and professional relationships; the toll it can take on all concerned can be devastating.

Every day within my work I see the shattering effects that mental illness can have on the sufferer and their loved ones, and every day I am continually confronted by the pain and trauma that mental illness can bring to the home environment. I have seen and experienced at first hand how it can rip families apart and drive a wedge through once solid relationships, bringing them crashing to their knees.

I will never forget when Samantha was in the throes of OCD how my husband Kevin described our everyday family life as being as if someone had picked our house up each morning and given it a good shake, bringing mindboggling chaos and turmoil with it for the rest of the day, until bedtime once again restored peace and calm – until the next day when the whole cycle would begin again! Equally, I can say from first-hand experience that, with the right support, understanding, patience and unconditional love, the damage can, in time, be repaired and family dynamics restored, bringing family members closer together and stronger than they ever were before. My family is a real example of this.

Chapter 7

The parent/carer

A mother's love
By Samantha Crilly

A feeling so spiritual, so unique
It watches over me when I sleep
Catches the bad dreams before they land
Strengthens me as it holds my hand
Surrounding me with love and hope
Putting faith inside me when I can't cope
By my side for when my demons appear
Be my shield for when they come near
To die before me with no fear...
Some say it's an angel looking down from above
But I know it's down here... it's my mother's love.

As a parent or carer, you will probably know your loved one inside-out, so witnessing their bizarre behaviours or hearing their irrational ruminations, totally out of character with the person you once knew, will undoubtedly be difficult to hear and painful to watch.

Kevin, Samantha's dad and my husband, says of how he felt:

> Watching my beautiful little girl being taken over by this terrible life-changing illness and drifting into her own crazy, mixed-up, shallow world, left me trying very hard not to get angry, but there was no one to get angry at.

The sufferer could potentially be afraid and even possibly embarrassed by what they are experiencing, as they may not understand what is happening to them themselves. Often, they are worrying about what people would think of them, if they knew what horrible and disturbing thoughts were really going through their minds.

133

Samantha comments:

> Although Dad tried to understand the OCD, I didn't want him to see it in case he thought it was weird, so I often avoided him.

Carrying this immense pressure around with them, and often not being able to see a way out, OCD sufferers can often turn to making up stories and playing with the truth, doing or saying whatever they can to make sure they cover their tracks. Some sufferers often go to extreme lengths to disguise their illness; they can become uncharacteristically deceptive and sneaky, leaving the carer/loved one continually second guessing, and doubting most of the 'truths' the sufferer supposedly offers. As hard as it is, try not to let this behaviour sabotage your mutual trust, remembering it is the OCD you are fighting, not the person.

As a parent or carer, I would imagine that, if your life is anything like mine was, compromises, challenges and sacrifices are now a part of your everyday existence and relationship with the sufferer. As you try to balance yourself and make sense of things that seem nonsensical, you will no doubt be finding it very difficult to know the right thing to say or do, overwhelmed as you must be by the enormity of an illness that you cannot physically see. As a parent or carer, you will probably be feeling as though you are walking on eggshells most of the time, worried that you may say the wrong thing, or concerned that your relationship with the sufferer is exacerbating the problem, enabling their compulsions. Try not to be afraid of what you cannot see, remembering that behind the OCD your loved one is still there, and they, not the OCD, would want you to fight on their behalf.

I found, in my own experience, that by learning as much as I could about the illness and the way that it was affecting Samantha, I was better equipped to handle and understand some of what Samantha was experiencing without being manipulated and divided by the illness. By researching and gaining as much knowledge as I could, I was able to strengthen my armour against the OCD permeating its way through. Be prepared for things potentially getting worse before they start to get better; it can often be a 'one step forward, two steps back' scenario. Try not to compare someone else's recovery with your loved one's, as there can be wide variations between people's responses to treatment; changes can be slow and gradual and unique to a particular person, but all are of equal importance. When small improvements take place, be sure to acknowledge them and voice your encouragement – it is one of your strongest tools in keeping your relationship with the sufferer as tight as possible. I know it was for me.

Your natural instinct will be to protect the person you love from suffering and to take away their pain and confusion, but when faced with the demons that are mental illness this is probably the hardest fight you will ever be faced with… it was for me. Your immediate reaction will be to question yourself: 'What did I do wrong?' 'What could I have done differently?' 'Is it my fault?' Before we go any further, from what I have learnt, both personally and professionally, I can honestly say that most of the time parents, siblings or loved ones are not, and I repeat *NOT*, to blame – despite how others, sometimes, may make us feel. Mental health issues are just one of those things that sadly seem to affect some people and not others. So please, before you read any further, as hard as it may be, try to stop blaming yourself; it can only be a waste of your precious time and energy, which can be put to better and more positive use.

When I first realised the extent of the OCD and how much Samantha needed me again, I experienced many different emotions, from being scared, angry, alone and frightened, to even a bit resentful that she was struggling again; despite these feelings, I knew, as her mum, that I had no choice but to find the strength to step up to the mark again to support her.

Samantha says how relieved she felt, once she did eventually open up:

> Mum, being very intuitive, knew something was wrong, I finally told her everything and she got into 'super mum' mode to help me get better.

It is hard enough to admit inwardly to yourself, let alone outwardly to others, that your loved one is mentally ill... again. It is important to acknowledge that all of these feelings are perfectly normal, and it does not mean you love the person suffering any less; it is all part of the process of working through and beyond an illness that is just as serious as any physically visible condition.

I knew deep down that my husband, Kevin, was not going to handle it at all well, mainly due to his straightforward nature and lack of understanding of mental illness. He loves his daughter to bits, in fact in the early years they were quite the team, doing everything together, going on little mini-adventures and loving life. Despite Kevin also noticing slight changes in Samantha's behaviour a second time around, he still found it hard to see that there was a real issue with her. Had it been a physical injury or illness that he could both see and understand, like the time she broke her elbow on the trampoline and he was her absolute hero for saving her, he would have stepped up to the mark without hesitation, but mental illness does not affect the elbow, or any other bones or outer layers, it affects the mind.

Looking back, I think he too resented the illness, as he felt it had stolen his daughter from him, which, for the time Samantha was ill, it had. Their relationship suffered greatly for many years as Samantha struggled to be around him, knowing that he just did not understand her, and Kevin battled to get his head around the whole thing, feeling helpless as he watched his daughter fall into the ever-open arms of OCD and mental illness. As a mother and a wife, I attempted to balance everything to keep my family afloat. I was looking after Samantha, whilst being constantly on edge around my loving husband and worrying about my other daughter, Samantha's twin sister, Charlotte, who was quite rightly suffering in her own way, quietly, and needed her mum too. However, the consequences of Samantha's illness, coupled with Kevin's bewilderment and Charlotte's distress, had devastating effects on the family dynamics and with not enough hours in each day for me to accommodate and help everyone, I was constantly exhausted. In a desperate bid to channel all my time and effort into my girls and Samantha's recovery, and to try to salvage my own sanity, I asked Kevin, my husband, my soul-mate, my everything, to leave. He did not, thank goodness! Looking back, that was a turning point for all of us – we could not have reached a lower point, we were broken, but there was only one direction left for us to go and that was 'up'. Together, as a family.

From then on, standing up to the OCD and not being afraid to challenge it helped us enormously. As expected, it caused all manner of arguments and heated discussions, but with Samantha's perseverance and determination to fight the OCD, we were not letting it get in our way any longer.

Kevin reflects back and shares his thoughts:

It can make the simple things in life so difficult and frustrating for the whole family, it can make or break a family, but If you can accept the problem they have and try to help them, then slowly things do get better.

Samantha adds:

Things changed very gradually with Dad as I began to open up a bit more and he tried to understand it a bit more. I still know he doesn't understand it, but he does what he can to make situations easier for me when he can. This is something that has helped to rebuild our relationship back to where it was.

We were far more powerful as a united family unit than the illness that was ravaging our daughter's mental health. We held on tight to the hope that Samantha was going to get better whilst reminding ourselves that we each too had a life outside of and independent of OCD.

The healing process is unique to every individual so there are no time constraints on how long the recovery time will be. It is therefore really important to try to continue doing the fun things you previously did as a family, such as the cinema, museums, shopping – anything to keep the natural momentum going.

Charlotte says of how she looked forward to spending time together:

> Every weekend Mum made sure we spent time together as a family, doing things we all enjoyed. This was a highlight of my week, and I think helped us stay connected.

Samantha echoes Charlotte's thoughts, and says:

> The time we spent together as a family motivated me to push forward with my recovery; it reminded me of what I was missing out on and what could be.

Ensure that the outings are OCD-free zones (as much as possible), where the subject is neither acknowledged nor discussed, to enable both the sufferer and their loved ones to enjoy just being together in some shape or form of normality.

Kevin to this day does not fully understand what goes on in Samantha's head but I have to say, he has taken the time to try and understand her, to learn to go along with certain things and not to question her. Situations are now approached with humour, openness and love, which has led them to a mutual acceptance. They are making good out of something not so good, if that makes sense! At times, I wondered if we would make it out the other side as a complete family, but we have done, and so can you.

Kevin wanted to add:

> I have been around mental illness for years and, as much as I have tried, I still don't get it. What I do know now is that if it isn't treated and the person doesn't receive help, it's not going to go away and could manifest into something much worse! Thankfully, my lovely Sam is back with us now, from wherever she was.

Siblings

That leads me straight onto our other daughter, Samantha's twin sister Charlotte, who has always loved and supported her sister unconditionally as best she could with her sunny, positive, uplifting nature. It is important to remember here that siblings struggle just as much as the sufferer, if not more at times, as they not only witness the pain their loved one is going through, but feel pain themselves as they become unintentionally side-lined as a result of the sufferer becoming the main focus of concern for those around them.

Charlotte talks of how it took her time to get her head around and accept the mental illness:

> It took me time to understand the OCD, but I now feel I understand it as much as I possibly can without having had the illness myself. The way I found it easiest to understand was by listening to my sister with no judgement, no snap answers and a little humour at times of need.

Being twins, my daughters have a unique connection, something quite special, so when Samantha started to face the challenges and tried to cover up the OCD so that none of us would realise what was happening, Charlotte suspected all was not well with her, and put out an olive branch to encourage Samantha to have the confidence to start the much-needed conversation.

Samantha would often struggle to sleep through the chaos inside her head and would seek solace by clambering into Charlotte's bed with her, where she felt safe from her troubled thoughts and could sleep peacefully.

Once Samantha's condition was out in the open, Charlotte gave up much of her own life to help her sister heal with all the love and support she could give, never leaving her side, always putting Samantha's needs before her own. Our whole family have given parts, if not all, of our lives at times to make our home a safe environment for Samantha to be able to relax and readjust her head and mind, which was critical for her, preparing her psychologically for her next mentally challenging hurdle.

Charlotte, shares her thoughts:

> In my own experience, OCD affects the whole family, close friends and everyone in the surrounding support group. You are constantly aware, thinking, researching and learning about the illness, trying your hardest to support your loved one in as many ways as you can. We have all given up pieces of our lives to enable us to support my sister, but we all know if it were the other way around she would do no less for us.

Siblings may have different thoughts, questions and concerns that will need acknowledging and talking about openly. They may be scared or frightened for their brother/sister who is struggling with a mental illness; they will probably be worried about their parents and how they are coping, whilst also being concerned for their own future and that of their siblings, fearful of the unknown and uncertain of what it will bring for everyone involved. They may feel anger, frustration and a little embarrassed at the prospect of what others may think and say. I can wholeheartedly say that all these thoughts and feelings are perfectly natural and understandable, and if used positively can lead to valuable life skills going forward.

It is important that siblings can be allowed to participate to a certain degree in the recovery process to help them remain hopeful about the future, but only if they want to be, as their thoughts and decisions need to be respected at all times. Helping their sibling will also give them a sense of achievement and inclusion and increase their own self-worth.

Charlotte offers advice from her own personal experience:

> My advice to other siblings would be to create a safe and supportive atmosphere for your troubled sibling and understand that they do not want the OCD just as much as you don't want them to have it. Show them pieces of life they can have outside of the mental illness, talk about your interests and how your day was (don't always expect a long answer or too much interaction). Be non-judgemental and listen without prejudice, no matter how difficult the situation. Find someone you trust who you can talk to and open up with so it doesn't build up inside you. Lastly, always have hope that the mental illness will slowly leave, and your sibling will come back to you; it just takes time, patience and resilience.

My girls are now 26 years old and the love they share remains as strong as ever due in part to Charlotte's involvement in Samantha's recovery. I feel incredibly blessed that it has strengthened their bond, not weakened it.

Sam speaks of her love for her sister:

> Charlie [Charlotte] and I have always been unconditionally close but when I started to really get into my recovery that was when we really started to get our relationship back. It was all about me opening up about it and Charlie wanting to listen and understand. She never judged me; she just wanted to help and took on board everything I said. This made it a lot easier to go out in social situations and to be able to do stuff together as she knew what I was able to do and what I wasn't and what I would find hard. Thus, she put me at my ease so I was able to be myself rather than have a voice in the back of my head telling me something was wrong. Charlie and I often laugh about it and joke as well, which always takes the edge off it a bit!

Charlotte powerfully concludes:

> For my sister and I, in the end, it has made us closer than ever; she is my best friend. I don't know where we would be or what we would be doing today if it wasn't for the mental illnesses and what we have gone through, but I do know, now it has almost come to an end, I wouldn't want to be anywhere else.

Extended family members

It is difficult for those closest to someone suffering from a mental illness such as OCD to understand what is happening to their loved ones. However, it is probably even more confusing for extended family members and friends who do not witness the day-to-day complexities of the condition. From an extended family member's perspective, they will firstly see the disruption, followed by the distress of the immediate family concerned as they slowly isolate themselves from the outside world, struggling to come to terms with the change within their family. This is not to suggest that the closest carers do not want or need any help; it may be that they are just exhausted from living within the confines of the illness. Let them know that help is available, if and when they are ready.

It may take those outside the immediate family a while to accept and understand that OCD has a neurobiological basis, and that their loved one's brain is not functioning in the same way as the brain of someone who does not have OCD. The sufferer is no more at fault for having the disorder than are those who suffer from other medical conditions, such as asthma or diabetes.

Encouragement, love, non-judgement and understanding are paramount.

Speaking from my own experience, my parents initially found it very difficult to get their heads around the fact that their granddaughter was suffering from OCD, the distorted way of thinking and how this affected her. Being from a generation in which mental illness was not spoken of and family matters were kept very private it was difficult and confusing for them both, but despite their uncertainty, they listened without judgement, offering nothing but love, encouragement and support, which has been priceless to Samantha and the family as a whole. My mum in particular went above and beyond what anyone might expect, and as hard as she found it sometimes, she never lost hope that Samantha would make a recovery.

My mum, Samantha's grandma, describes how she felt through the journey:

> In the beginning, frightened and useless – after all, it's a mental illness, an illness that can't be seen.
>
> As a little understanding came about, I felt unsure as to the best way to help.
>
> As time goes by, and with more understanding through talking with Sam – ease and more self-assurance and confidence creeps in.

Samantha says of how the OCD has brought her closer to her grandma:

> Grandma always wanted to understand and listened to every bit; she never judged and just wanted to 'get' it. She always tried to put herself in my shoes and relate to my problems herself and what she has been through in life. Grandma never asked for what I couldn't give her; we would talk about so much random stuff as well, like when she was growing up, so it would take my mind off things that were going on in my head.

My mum concludes:

> We have become closer during this long journey, the reason being we can talk as equals and listen and accept. She tells me her thoughts; I tell her mine. We laugh when we say or hear something funny and we hug when it is sad.

Romantic relationships

Some adult sufferers of OCD struggle with striking up and holding onto romantic relationships, with many subconsciously pushing people away rather than living with the stigma and the misunderstandings that can halt any romantic union. From the sufferer's perspective, they may be living a highly structured life and feel trapped – cut off from the outside world in order to hide the nature of their obsessions and compulsions. They will want to avoid rejection by a current or potential partner, or by a loved-one or colleague. This other person may even be the one around whom their obsessions and compulsions revolve, posing challenges with the contact and intimacy that are needed in relationships. Periods of depression may also be contributing to their condition, making it virtually impossible to maintain any relationships, romantic or otherwise. It is paramount in any relationship that the carers and loved-ones are involved as much as the sufferer will allow, encouraging them to be as open and honest as possible. The more you learn about the sufferer and their OCD, the more the mutual trust and understanding will grow and strengthen.

Jay, Samantha's boyfriend, shares his thoughts:

> I still have much to learn. I may not understand why Sam feels that way about a certain thing, but sometimes neither does she. So simply accepting that's the way her mind thinks at the moment and, when she fully understands it, believing she will educate me on it. Seeking knowledge from websites and books or talking to counsellors or carers can help you expand your knowledge of OCD.

Everyone can find love and be loved. Someone suffering from OCD, wanting a relationship to work, must be ready potentially to expose that vulnerability and be prepared for the risk of getting hurt or being rejected. Everyone is in the same boat where new relationships are concerned: we all have flaws, insecurities and quirks. Before embarking on a potentially successful relationship, it is important that the sufferer feels as confident as possible in themselves and what they have to offer. Therapy and behavioural treatment groups can help them to disassociate themselves from the OCD, enabling their personality to shine through. These types of session are a good starting point where sufferers can talk openly to other OCD sufferers, to find out how they cope with dating, relationships and friendships. Focusing on carefully managing their condition and reducing their symptoms first, will, in time, enable them to begin to enjoy life again, boosting their confidence levels – which in itself is an attractive quality – and helping them socialise with others, including potential love interests!

I have seen at first hand how toxic and destructive relationships can be when you have two people together suffering from mental illness, and although never intentional, the illnesses can feed off each other in a negative way, so bringing both people down with it.

Samantha says of her own personal experience:

Having been in a relationship with someone who shared the same demons, it soon became apparent that they [the demons] had become best friends... with a mission to destroy us. Feeling trapped, and for my own sanity and wellbeing, the only option I had was to break free. This allowed me to start rebuilding myself back to health.

However, in some cases, it can work the opposite way and, if the foundations are strong enough, two people can work together to make it a success.

Peggy says of her marriage:

Luckily I am married to a fellow Alien! He is obsessively tidy and a mad keen house-hubby – it is a dream to be honest! We don't clash as my obsessions revolve around hyperactive creativity. It is a match made in heaven.

My daughter Samantha now has a wonderful young man in her life. Due to her past experiences and not wanting the OCD to dominate her life and her relationships, it has taken Samantha some time to let him in. Her fear of being judged and thought to be a burden outweighed her desire to open up to him for quite a while, but with his patience, love, support and encouragement, and his wish to understand, she has learnt to put her trust in him.

Jay offers some words of wisdom:

It is difficult to know when to challenge or talk to your partner about their obsessions or just to allow them to happen. As a partner, I want to understand Sam's illness and how her mind processes these thoughts, but surely sufferers do not want to talk about every challenge they face and what they're feeling as they may fear having to justify themselves when there is no justifiable reason; what they are experiencing is a compulsion. Rather than questioning what is going through a sufferer's mind, using a simple question like 'Is everything okay?' gives your partner an opportunity to talk at their discretion.

With time, his love for her has allowed her to relax more and be herself, which in turn has helped the OCD to subside. This is wonderful, not just for Samantha but for all of us as it has led her to embrace and experience things she never thought possible, let alone enjoy.

So, with this in mind, I believe that the right relationship with the right person can add positivity, confidence and assurance to the recovery process, in ways that family members cannot. If the circumstances present themselves and the sufferer feels ready both emotionally and mentally, then I think they should welcome the possibility of letting a new kind of love into their hearts, as this is just one of life's natural progressions. Samantha and Jay would like to end with the following comments. Jay says:

> As a partner, it didn't really affect me, I understood that these are the conditions that our relationship have to be set on and there may be some complications on the way, but is my partner worth it, *most definitely!* Again, accepting that this is the way Sam's mind/illness works and I'm here to help in any way possible. Of course, I don't want Sam to suffer from the condition for the rest of her life and I will challenge her if needed, but it's set at her pace and when she feels it's in a safe environment.

Samantha says of Jay's unconditional support:

> Jay's unconditional love and care have enabled me to do things I could only ever have dreamed of before. His non-judgemental ways have helped me feel comfortable in my own skin, so enabling me to be myself all the time. Being so relaxed around him and knowing and feeling how much he loves me for who I really am, quirks and all, has played a huge part in my recovery. He always has my back, never questioning me, and is always keen to understand me and how my mind works. Most importantly, being with Jay has enabled me to see ahead more clearly; I now know that I can have a future with someone – hopefully him.

Friendships

Much has been written about sufferers of OCD and their immediate family, but much less has been written about the close friends who have to watch the sufferer struggle through the effects of their condition. The knock-on effects of OCD extend far beyond the inner circle of the sufferer. I would advise that you research and learn all you can about what your friend might be feeling, so that you can get a better understanding; this will enable you to offer friendship and support to them in the best way possible. All they need from you is patience, listening without judgement and lots of love. On some occasions, the sufferer may not wish to discuss their illness with you; they may just want you to be their piece of normality – their one connection to a life they once recognised, a life before their mental illness. This connection will give them hope, so try to engage in everyday conversations, things that you share a common interest in, or even just everyday mundane things that they will listen to, to escape the confines of their disturbing thoughts and rituals. Do not expect too much from them in return, though; there will be a long road travelled, but as long as they know you have their back and are there for them it will bring comfort to them in their dark times. There will be good days and bad days, periods of hopefulness and hopelessness, so the sufferer's emotions, and yours, will fluctuate up and down as they make strides in the fight against their illness. If your friend is also taking medication to help with the effects of OCD, there may be extra emotional turbulence so be prepared for it. Above all, positivity is the key; in fact, it is the most valuable thing you can offer your friend. They will respond far better and more quickly without negativity and pessimism. Remember, your friend does not want this mental illness that consumes and overwhelms them just as much as you do not want them to have it. Keep reassuring, praising and encouraging them that recovery is possible; they need to be aware that they have a team supporting them, willing them to get better. In this case, it really does take a village, not an individual. Communicate positively, directly and clearly; be kind and patient and a sign of strength, not weakness.

Mental illness can not only impact on the sufferer's relationships and friendships, but it can also have a negative effect on the carer's relationships and friendships. From my own experience, some of my own friendships have drifted, partly due to the fact that, as a carer, I felt continually drained, tired and a bit low, so I was not always able to engage fully. Thankfully, I have many friends who have been supportive, understanding and patient and loved me unconditionally;   I am incredibly blessed to have them around me.

Chapter 7

One of my best friends, Kate, who has been by my side the whole time, says:

> Being there for Lynn can mean simply being at the other end of the phone, going out for a coffee after work or being understanding if she has to cancel an arrangement. I also try to remind Lynn of the importance of having a break once in a while as well, so she can recharge her batteries. Hopefully she knows that I am always there for her no matter what.

Another of my best friends, Wendy, follows with:

> I have known Lynn for over 20 years, and have been there through the good and the bad times. As her friend, I have always been there for her as a listening ear, with a glass of wine, whenever she needed it.

My daughter Samantha has been blessed with two very loyal friends, Kim and Zoe, who have stuck by her since their younger years. Both girls have played a pivotal part in her recovery process, never asking more of her than she could give, even when they themselves did not fully understand her at times. They have never judged her, only accepted and loved her for who she is, seeing beyond the OCD and being there for her unconditionally.

Sam says of her love for her friends:

> Over the years, both Zoe and Kim have always supported and loved me unconditionally, always being open minded and never judging me, even for the craziest of things, and always being understanding. There have been times when I have had to cancel plans at the last minute, but in the end, I found that being honest about why I couldn't go has strengthened the friendships. They are the best friends I could ask for.

Kim speaks of their friendship:

Sam is someone who is very close to my heart. I do not know the ins and out of what she has been through, but what I do know is that we would never question each other and trust that there is a reason for everything. We understand each other's strengths and weaknesses and use this to lift each other up as opposed to judging each other, this is invaluable! Sam is a true friend who I will always cherish.

Zoe powerfully concludes:

In truth, Sam suffering from mental illness does add a complication to our friendship. It is a subject that I try to, but often can't fully, comprehend. There's almost an unspoken agreement between us – I won't always understand what she's going through and she won't always be able to commit to doing things. We don't have to talk about it, but we can when she wants to. The end result is a best friend who is great in so many other ways, and mental illness is an accepted part of that friendship. It's similar to a friend in a foreign country or a friend with a new baby; it can be difficult to maintain a connection sometimes. But stand by a friend with mental illness, because when they are ready, they will be one of the most tenacious, courageous people you will get the honour of being friends with.

Workplace

Mental illness can also affect people in the work environment. Even though there is far more awareness and less discrimination against mental health issues in the workplace than there used to be, the very nature of this 'silent' issue means there is more pressure to verbalise and share with colleagues just what the sufferer and their family are going through in order for people in the workplace to have a clearer understanding of the sufferer's behaviour and thought processes. With most physical illnesses, your symptoms are clearly visible, but with mental illness you have to speak openly about your limitations and/or potential triggers to validate your need for extra flexibility within the working hours and other restrictions.

While organisations are being encouraged to be more supportive of mental health issues, often the individual member of staff to whom the sufferer, or their carers, has to report, may have very little personal experience of the subject, potentially exacerbating the situation even more. Sometimes the intensity of OCD can bring on crippling social anxiety; some sufferers might find it hard to perform their roles within the working environment and to maintain healthy working relationships, to the point that they may struggle to communicate with their colleagues, speak openly during meetings or attend work-related social gatherings such as after-work drinks and birthday celebrations. Try not to judge; it is their choice, which must always be respected.

Emma tells us of her experience at work:

> Having suffered OCD for many years now, I have found it very difficult to hold down a permanent job, until recently. I have been very lucky to have had an understanding line manager in my current position, who I feel I can go to when I am struggling the most. My manager has been very proactive about putting things in place when I feel I cannot perform to my best, which has made coping with the OCD and working so much easier.

I would like to add, whether you are a parent or sibling, a partner or carer, a friend or work colleague, the road to recovery is long; it takes time to travel it and the experience cannot be sugar-coated; but having someone walk those miles with you, however rocky, can make all the difference.

Samantha would like to conclude this chapter with:

> Although I have had my fair share of mental health issues and challenges, I have also been incredibly blessed to have such wonderful family and friends around me; I am not sure where I would be now without them.

My mum, in particular, no matter how bad it got, has always been by my side, with her unconditional, non-judgemental love, never giving up, always supporting and encouraging. This, over time, has given me the strength, determination and courage to push forward and believe in myself and the spirit to recover and get my life back. Although not an easy journey, it has been one worth making and I can honestly say it was a fight I am glad I took on and won!

Chapter 8

OCD and children

It can be quite common for children, when they are young, to subconsciously repeat things over and over – for example, always choosing the same hiding place in a hide-and-seek game, watching the same television programmes on repeat, or telling the same joke over and over again. It can also be an everyday commonality to have set and timed routines around mealtimes, bath times and bedtimes, so giving a child structure to their day. These predictable routines can enable children to have a sense of safety and security which they will normally be soothed and comforted by. However, for children suffering from OCD, the reasons behind repetition and routine can be very different.

When a child is suffering from OCD, these routines can, unintentionally, become ways of encouraging the fears and anxieties which the OCD has subconsciously created. Whilst worry and fear are common in childhood, it can become an issue when they begin to interfere with a child's ability to engage in 'normal' activities and behaviours which are appropriate to their age.

OCD in children is so much more than the stereotypical hand-washing: it encompasses thoughts and impulses that can get trapped in a child's mind, creating a sense of uneasiness within themselves and their way of thinking. To appease the 'horrible thoughts' and attempt to rid themselves of the constant noise that is in their head, a child can subconsciously start to perform rituals in the hope of avoiding anything negative happening, to them or the people around them.

Paul looks back at his early signs of OCD in his childhood:

> When I was very young I remember touching everything three times, and if I touched things differently I had to repeat the process. As a teenager, I was diagnosed with OCD – with me it was to do with thoughts and I had to run through certain thought patterns.

According to Bright Tots, approximately one child in every 200 suffers from OCD, with the onset of symptoms starting as early as the age of three.[11] However, due to the lack of their vocal development and ability to communicate, it can make it more difficult to diagnose. Most children above the age of six who may be suffering from OCD will most likely already be displaying visible signs and can be better equipped to communicate; diagnosis may therefore be easier.

Looking back, Natasha realises:

> The crisis point came when I was about 17, but when I look back there were signs from a much earlier age, probably seven or eight.

It is important to remember that OCD is a neurological problem and there probably is not anything either you or your child could have done to cause the onset: it is related to the brains chemistry and function, and is in fact a very treatable condition. Your child's successes and future do not have to be limited by this condition if the right intervention and treatment are sought as early as possible.

In the very early stages, the parent or carer may not even notice that there is a change happening within their child; it is more likely that even the child will not be aware at first because they may be thinking that their experiences and thoughts are common. At the point when the anxiety begins to kick in and the child begins to subconsciously relinquish control to the OCD, they may realise that some of their behaviour is different from most other children around them.

Family and everyday life can be hectic and full-on at the best of times, and sometimes, unintentionally, families and loved ones can become used to a child's rituals and compulsions without realising they are anything unusual, inadvertently making allowances and accommodating them. For example:

- Parents/carers may unconsciously begin adding extra time allowances to their day to accommodate their child's ever-expanding behaviour patterns.
- Parents'/carers' routines may unconsciously become compromised as they try to avoid locations and circumstances that can be seen to trigger their child's worries, fears and anxiety.

Perhaps, if any of the above resonates with you and your life is being disrupted or controlled in this way, it may be time to re-evaluate what could potentially be going on. From past experience, I know myself how easy it is to say, 'I will deal with it tomorrow', but please remember, like all mental illnesses, time is of the essence and waits for no one.

OCD is like a spoilt child, never satisfied and always wanting more. Whatever a child does to pacify and temporarily silence the thoughts and urges, it generally only perpetuates the cycle as feelings of incompleteness repeatedly come to the forefront of the child's mind, reinforcing his/her need to perform the ritual again, which in turn will only feed the OCD, making it stronger.

Physically and mentally your child's time may gradually become consumed by the intensity of the OCD symptoms, which in themselves can be draining and affect quality of sleep and sleep patterns. The constant chaos, on replay inside a child's head, can be exhausting, particularly at bedtime, when the brain should be recharging itself and resting. The constant lack of much-needed rest and recuperation can lead to the child being over-tired and unable to think straight, all of which can have a negative impact on their general and everyday functioning, often getting in the way of the important things, such as school, extra-curricular activities and friendships, and affecting family life.

There is a distinct line between the behavioural patterns of a 'quirky' child and those of a child who is beginning to develop OCD. Most children have a tendency to line up their toys in some form of random order without any particular reason or expected outcome as to why. However, a child with OCD may do so because they believe if one toy is placed in the wrong position, thus upsetting the order, it will cause something bad to happen, usually to them or a loved one. Another example would be a child running up and down the stairs for fun in contrast with a child with OCD who would use those specific repetitions to avoid any negative consequences.

Carol looks back at the beginnings of her son's OCD:

> Steven loved his toy cars. I remember he used to line them up in colour order in certain places in his bedroom. If anyone wanted to play with them and moved them out of order, he would become very agitated and upset, to the point that we made sure we didn't touch the cars. In hindsight, I now realise that his behaviour was the start of his OCD, which escalated in his teens.

Obsessions exist as thoughts, urges or images that a child does not want, but as much as he or she tries, he/she cannot get them out of his/her head. Sometimes these obsessions can make a child feel nervous or unsettled. For example, the child may:

*   worry about germs on toys or door handles, or about uncleanliness in general
*   worry about illness and death of family, friends or even themselves

- experience distressing thoughts and images about inflicting harm on others
- have constant feelings that something bad is going to happen.

Compulsions are actions a child will perform over and over again, not necessarily because they want to, but because they feel as if they have to, in order to relieve their scary, obsessive thoughts and feelings. These actions can often develop into rituals, meaning they have to be completed the same way each and every time, over and over again. Sometimes, when a ritual has completed its cycle, the child can be 'tricked' into thinking that the OCD has passed; however, it is not uncommon for one ritual to be immediately replaced by another, so please remember it is important to be mindful of this.

Some common examples of compulsions might include the child:

- excessively checking and rechecking certain things
- excessively washing themselves and constantly cleaning their teeth
- continually repeating actions until they feel 'just right'
- continually arranging and re-arranging certain items
- repeating lucky words or numbers
- excessively seeking reassurance (e.g. 'Are you sure it is going to be okay?')
- excessively counting or tapping
- being reluctant to throw anything away, even if the item is broken, damaged or no longer useful.

Unfortunately, OCD will not disappear on its own, and in some cases children who suffer from it will go on to have other mental health issues later in life. Interestingly, nearly one third to half of all adult sufferers found that their condition had stemmed from their childhood. Therefore, seeking professional help and treatment for your child at the earliest stage possible is paramount for their best chance of a full and long-term recovery.

OCD and school

School life can be both frightening and humiliating for a child with OCD, whatever stage they are at educationally. For their parents it can also be a time of worry and stress. At a time when focus and concentration are needed in the classroom, the interference of obsessive thoughts and compulsions can wreak havoc in every aspect of a child's school day.

Within a school setting, OCD symptoms can quite easily go unnoticed depending on the type of obsession. As some forms of OCD are not generally visible, the problem can prove difficult for teachers with little or no mental health training to recognise, and may be incorrectly dismissed as a 'phase', or as disruptive behaviour. In the classroom, a child suffering from OCD could be seen to be daydreaming, distracted or uninterested, giving the impression, perhaps, that they have an 'attitude' or are even lazy. At times, they may also appear unfocused and unable to concentrate on their school work; however, this is probably because they are preoccupied and busy focusing on their nagging urges or on the confusing, demanding and sometimes terrifying OCD thoughts and images that are on replay in their head. They may also be distracted by thoughts of having to complete rituals, either overtly or covertly, to relieve any distress or anxiety that they may be experiencing.

Tea Gray, secondary school teacher, comments:

> The most important thing a teacher can do (in my opinion) is to observe behaviour. Often OCD can manifest itself slowly and so jumping to conclusions can be detrimental. Keep an open channel of dialogue and don't be afraid to ask questions, but this must be done delicately as students will, in many cases, be embarrassed by their OCD behaviour. I also think

speaking to your school's 'safeguarding lead' is vital if the OCD behaviour puts any students at risk. The dialogue must also happen with the parents who sometimes might not have seen any OCD behaviour, as we know that young people can be very good at hiding things. When speaking to a student, reassure them that they are not alone, and that they are not 'crazy'. So many times students have been too afraid to talk because they believe that they are crazy and depressed and these are frightening terms to have to deal with as a young person. Being mindful of the delicate nature of what a child is thinking is important too.

Some common ways that OCD may present itself within the classroom environment can include the following. The child may:

- be disruptive in their behaviour, or have sudden outbursts of anger or even tantrums
- have a low attendance rate and/or frequently be late for school
- constantly adjust their desk and rearrange their stationery or other items in the classroom
- frequently ask to use the bathroom
- repeatedly ask the same questions
- have difficulty completing their school work
- go to extreme lengths to avoid certain places, situations, people or objects.

These behaviours can also affect a child's social environment as their peers will have little or no understanding of why they are behaving erratically. They could be seen as socially inappropriate or different, which potentially could lead to bullying or ridicule by others.

Hannah Arbuckle, a primary school teacher, offers us her thoughts:

Teaching a child with OCD can be a challenge. You want to accommodate the child's needs without drawing too much attention to the issue so that the other children do not notice that they are 'different'. The last thing you want is for the child to feel alienated when they are going through so many other things in their head at the same time. The most important thing is to be patient and understanding. Ensure the child is sat beside somebody who is considerate and supportive. Encourage the child to check that they have everything they need for the day and allow the child to set out their equipment in a way that suits them. Try and give the child a way to contact the teacher if things are getting too much that doesn't draw attention to the fact they need support. It may be a card that they turn up on the table or the child walking over to the classroom sink and signalling to the adults in the room that they need some time out or to talk. Most importantly, understand that the child has different needs to be catered for each day and that support should be offered where necessary.

If you have any concerns or worries about your child, it is vital that you try to open up a line of communication with the school. By doing so, hopefully the school will implement the correct procedures needed, in order to be able to fully support your child. Everyone working together as a team will enable your child to have the best possible chance of a positive school life.

Talking to your child about OCD

As a parent or carer, if you think or feel something is amiss with your child, then you are probably right. I always say that there is nothing more powerful than a parent's intuition and love. Do not be afraid to follow and act on your instincts.

Some valuable things to consider might include:

- have you noticed a decline in your child's self-confidence, particularly around friends?
- have they withdrawn from social activities such as dance classes, sports groups or after-school clubs?

- do they seem preoccupied and quiet, wanting to be in their own company more than usual?
- is their behaviour in complete contrast to how they used to be?
- do they often talk under their breath and mutter to themselves?

Due to their immaturity and lack of understanding, most children suffering from OCD will have difficulty in knowing how to talk and communicate about what is going on in their head. They may be confused, embarrassed and not able to process and understand the content of their thoughts and the reasoning behind the rituals that they find themselves compelled to do on a daily basis. At this point, the most effective way to help them is through communication. With this in mind, it is important to pick the right moment and location, and it should be at a time when it is just you and them, in a place where they feel relaxed, safe and secure.

When addressing the issues of OCD with a child, it is crucial that it is done on a level that they feel comfortable with and are able to understand. One way to help the child externalise their feelings and thoughts can be through story-telling. This can help the child to identify with what is happening to them, on a level that they can cope with.

For example, the child's OCD can be given a name. For now we can call it 'Mr Trouble', although I am sure that you have a few select names of your own!

Mr Trouble is a trickster and a bully. He likes to boss you around and tell you what to do, pretending to be your friend. He is not very nice and can be very unkind, making you feel nervous and worried about lots of things. He wants all your attention and makes you avoid certain situations, so he can make you follow his meaningless and silly rules. When you do what he asks he gets bigger and stronger and always wants more. Whatever you do, you will never make him happy. So, together we can be bigger and better than him. If we grow stronger and we fight him together, he will become smaller and weaker, and hopefully go away.

The story can be as long or as short as needed, and can be adapted to the child's intellectual level.

If your child is finding it difficult to verbalise their thoughts, encouraging them to draw or write down how they are feeling can sometimes be used as a different form of communication which can be just as effective as talking. This could help both of you to develop a better understanding of what is going on in their head. By communicating with them and listening to their responses you are giving them the confidence to open up about their feelings and emotions that are all interconnected with the OCD.

As a parent or carer, it is your natural instinct to want to try and fix any problem that a child may have. This can potentially make you over-zealous in your efforts to challenge and overcome the child's OCD for them. Unfortunately, this is not a battle you can take on alone on their behalf, nor will it be resolved overnight. It has to be a team effort, often including outside intervention; however, please remember, with lots of time and patience, it can be done.

OCD and teenagers

Teenage angst is a very common issue in pubescent young adults as they struggle to get to grips with the rapid hormonal and physical changes that their bodies are being subjected to. What once seemed to be a stereotypical sociable, relatively happy and engaging child can quickly become subdued, dramatic, over-sensitive, self-conscious, short-tempered and distant. These are all normal shifts in adolescence, as teenagers naturally try to find their own platform and independence, detached from the usual securities of their family unit.

Most teenagers will experience short-lived episodes of angst as they navigate their way through the challenging cross-over from childhood to being a young adult, and emotions such as sadness, anxiety and frustration will occasionally come to the forefront. Problems at school or with friendships and relationships can often be the main culprits, but usually these periods of anguish should only last for a short period of time. It is very hard to differentiate between what is normal behaviour for a teenager and what is not, but generally any prolonged and repeated episodes may be early warning signs of a more chronic problem, such as a mental health issue.

Aimee looks back, and says of her teenage years:

> During my teenage years, my parents and I had a very argumentative, explosive relationship. They assumed that my stubbornness and rigidity were my being 'difficult', when in fact I was trying to handle an immense amount of fear that I could not yet verbalise or express. I resisted change very much and could never do anything they asked of me because I had fixed in my mind the routines and procedures I HAD to do. My parents thought I was disobedient.

The difficulty in separating out and identifying a mental illness such as OCD, especially in a teenager, is that teenagers can seem reluctant to openly communicate with those closest to them, thus making an accurate diagnosis quite challenging. There are indicators, very similar to those of younger children suffering with OCD, in that the teenager will disengage from social and extra-curricular activities and become disconnected from the world around them, including family and close friends. Unbeknown to those around them, their lives will be consumed with symptoms, compulsions and obsessions, leaving little or no room for anything else. As the illness begins to get a hold of the sufferer, they may even manipulate others to enable them to hide the condition, telling lies to justify their unusual behaviour. This is not a reflection on them, and can be completely contradictory to the person they used to be, but very indicative of OCD.

Holly talks of her experience with her best friend who has recently been diagnosed with anxiety and OCD:

> Before my best friend was diagnosed with her OCD and anxiety, I was getting very worried about the way she was acting. She was being very 'all over the place', but at the same time seemed to be sort of trying to take control of things too. She also started to not tell me the truth about some things, which really upset me; she was always late to meet me, and I started to think she didn't want to be friends anymore. I did not want to give up on our friendship and knew something was not right with her, so I spoke to her mum about my concerns. Now she has a diagnosis and is receiving help, I can support her as my friend and hopefully help her return to her old self again.

There is no specific time for a worried parent or carer to wait before they intervene, but if you are unsure about the mental state of your teenager or someone close to you and you have a hunch that something is not quite right, then it should be investigated further. The most effective way to intervene at this point is through communication. As I have said, it is important to pick the right moment and location; it should be a time when it is just you and them, otherwise the young person may feel 'ganged up on'. It should also be a place where they feel safe; phones, tablets and laptops should all be switched off, so there is nothing to distract you or them. Young people often worry that by telling an adult, it will make things worse. You therefore need to be very clear from the start that you are there to support and help them, and that you will not do anything without discussing it with them first.

Communication should take place in a straightforward manner. Do not assume that you know what the problem is; you might be mistaken and could run the risk of talking for ages about something that they cannot relate to; let them tell you about their feelings and fears first.

The most important thing is not to judge them, whatever they might say to you. This may cause them to clam up. Show them that you respect their emotions and also their view point, even if you do disagree with certain things that they may be telling you.

Watching for reactions is important. You can tell when you have hit on a sore point or are getting close to an uncomfortable subject, by their eye contact, body language and how quick they are to defend themselves.

Remain calm. Although you are unlikely to feel calm inside, you must remain strong in the situation, because if you are not, the young person will start to panic. If you do not act as though there is a solution to their problem, and that everything will be okay, then they may start to despair; they are looking to you as someone to take their pain away.

Examples of how to start a much-needed conversation with them include:

- 'I have noticed that you are not quite your usual self at the moment... is something wrong?'
- 'You have been very quiet lately... is something troubling you?'
- 'Is there anything I can do to make life a bit easier for you?'
- 'Can you describe to me how you are feeling?'
- 'Would you rather write down how you are feeling on a piece of paper for me?'
- 'You have not seemed yourself recently; is there anything wrong?'

Acknowledge that the conversation is likely to be hard for them. Tell them that you are proud of the strength they are demonstrating in telling you about their issues. They might also be reassured if you tell them that there is nothing they could say that will make you stop loving them. Tell them it is okay to be frightened and they do not have to put on a brave face, because you will work it out together.

The sooner the teenager is given the correct skills and support to overcome the OCD, whether it be through books, professional help and/or the support of the family, school and/or college, the better the long-term prognosis will be.

Molly ends this chapter with her story of recovery:

From about the age of five I suffered from separation anxiety. As I got older, I began to find comfort in rituals, such as tapping the side of my bed a particular number of times each night before I went to bed. Soon this became somewhat of an obsession with a number of other rituals I followed, and suddenly I felt very out of control. I had convinced myself that something bad was going to happen if I didn't continuously follow all the set rituals for their set amount of times. At the age of 12, I was diagnosed with OCD and was given a book by the doctor who had diagnosed me. I was told to write down all the rituals I followed throughout the day, which consisted of about 25 different rituals (from checking behind a towel rail, to turning the light on and off a set amount of times). Next to each ritual I was told to mark the ritual each time I did it (which was 14 times). The doctor told me to take away a mark everyday so that I was still carrying out the ritual but one mark less each day. I eventually got to the day that I had no more marks next to any of the rituals, and nothing bad had happened. It was as simple as that, and the OCD hasn't returned since.

Chapter 9

OCD in the home

As we have already explored previously, living with someone suffering from OCD is like having an unwanted squatter move in, bringing all their baggage and staying indefinitely, causing chaos and turmoil to the home environment. The impact that this can have on all family members can be devastating, as Marilyn tells us:

> We are just a normal family with three beautiful girls. The illness of our middle daughter, Phoebe, started three years ago now and not only has it been an uphill battle and struggle for survival for Phoebe against the OCD, eating disorder, and suicidal thoughts, but it has ripped through the family and destroyed the family life we once had.
>
> It seems that through this nasty, aggressive, destructive and selfish illness, we have all had one goal – to get Phoebe better. But what about everyone else it has ripped through? The family it has torn apart; the devastation it has left behind? Phoebe gets all the help we can find for her and hopefully one day she will be through it and continue to lead a full and happy life. But then what about everyone else? The broken pieces she leaves in her trail: the sisters, the dad, the mum – who picks up these pieces? One life hopefully saved and put back together... and another four knocked to pieces.
>
> This illness is not just the burden of the individual, but of the whole family surrounding them who live through it all day and every day. I will never stop fighting for Phoebe, but hope we can also all pull it back as a family and have the life we once had.

It can be extremely stressful and put an enormous strain on relationships, which can, in turn, deteriorate as the OCD intensifies and manipulates the sufferer, so affecting the home and everyone residing within it. As a carer/parent/partner or friend, your role in being able to support the sufferer is of utmost importance and value. Having experienced some of what you are going through and some of the mixed emotions and fear of the unknown that you are probably feeling, I cannot reiterate enough the importance of unconditional love, patience, understanding and avoidance of judgement from all involved within the family home. This is something I know is sometimes easier said than done, when trying to live united in a household where OCD seems, and probably is, in control.

Everyday family life can be disrupted, and everybody within it may have to make certain changes to accommodate the ongoing recovery of the person struggling; this could potentially upset the family dynamics and stability.

Aimee's speaks of how her OCD affects her everyday family life:

> My OCD prevents me from socialising with friends and family. I am very limited as to what I can do day to day, as I have so many rules and a strict routine of what I feel I have to do. I am very isolated and have missed out on many things.

Aimee's mum, Ann, says:

> We can't do anything on the spur of the moment. She always has to plan ahead. If we go to family for the day to eat, we have to consider the times and question what and when we will be eating so it fits into her regime – her set times of eating. She usually has to leave at a certain time so she can get back to do her 'things'.

Being able to establish a positive, emotional balance in the home is pivotal for the person suffering, and for the family as a whole, something I know again is easier said than done. Trying to strengthen family relationships and promote a genuine acceptance, understanding and co-operation within the household for everyone living within it can be a challenging task – especially for the person trying to facilitate it. I have listed below some suggestions and ideas, with the hope of giving you the benefit of my own personal experience and providing you with tools for family members to help cope with some of the challenges of living with a person with OCD.

Recognise the warning signs

As we already know, OCD is a mental illness, therefore it is not always visible to the outsider or easy to identify. As my mum says:

> The sufferer can seem to the onlooker to be normal (whatever normal is!) and happy even – not relaying the agonising turmoil he/she is fighting with in his/her head as well as having to deal with the ups and downs of everyday life.

In my opinion, behavioural changes are one of the biggest signs that something is amiss. As busy as family life can be, it is vital not to dismiss any significant changes that could quite easily go unnoticed in your loved one or be dismissed as 'just their personality'. It is important to remember that these changes can develop slowly, but, with time, they could advance into something bigger and more sinister.

Helen, mother and carer to Poppy, picked up that all was not quite right at an early stage, and says:

> I noticed over the summer period that Poppy was very distant and seemingly preoccupied. Her behaviour was becoming quite erratic, with noticeable high levels of anxiety. She was doing things like jumping up and down, tapping surfaces and counting

out loud. If she was interrupted she became agitated and had to start again. I sat down to talk with her, and whilst not really understanding why she was doing it, she agreed that it was becoming overwhelming and she felt as though it was taking her over. At that point, I made an appointment with the GP, who then referred us for CBT sessions.

Some signs to be aware of are listed as follows. The person may:

1. not be able to account for large amounts of time spent on their own (in the bathroom, getting dressed, doing homework, cooking); they seemingly just 'lose time';
2. start to stay up late to 'get things done';
3. have poor time-keeping and start often to be late;
4. experience poor short-term memory;
5. experience the inability to sleep properly or constantly complain of being tired;
6. become withdrawn and constantly pre-occupied;
7. experience increased irritability and indecisiveness;
8. start doing things over and over again, never seeming to get a task finished;
9. constantly seek reassurance;
10. be always seemingly 'busy', but nothing gets done.

Avoid making personal criticism

The way in which you react to your loved one's OCD symptoms and behaviours can have a big impact on them and how they feel. Often, sufferers of OCD are already harbouring a lot of self-blame and judgement on themselves, so, when criticised or blamed for their behaviour, their symptoms can get worse. This could partly be because these emotions generate more anxiety, thereby leading to the thoughts being intensified. I know myself how frustrating and difficult it can be for the family members;

try to detach yourself from the behaviours and view them as the OCD and not as personality traits of your loved one, always remembering that your loved one is still inside. Hopefully, by doing this, it will enable you, the carer, to connect with the sufferer, rather than become alienated from them. Remember, it is the OCD you are fighting, not each other.

Acknowledge small steps forward

Most people thrive on praise; OCD sufferers are no different. The energy and effort it takes to accomplish something, such as washing their hands one less time or resisting asking for reassurance one more time, warrants positive recognition. While these improvements may seem insignificant and small to the family members, it will have been a very big step forward for the sufferer.

Helen tells us what worked for her and Poppy:

> Poppy and I sat down and discussed what we could do as a family to help her get through her OCD. We came up with the idea of a star chart, whereby every positive move forward was recognised and celebrated with a star. With a full star chart, we promised a family day out of her choice. This worked all round for Poppy and the family.

Poppy adds:

> The star chart gave me something positive to focus on, which made challenging my OCD worthwhile. It gave me a sense of fulfilment from being able to see the stars being crossed off, and knowing what I had achieved to get them.

Acknowledgments of these seemingly small accomplishments can be a powerful tool that encourages sufferers to keep trying and not give up. It can also let them know that their hard work and efforts to recover are being recognised.

Beware of reinforcing OCD behaviour

Family and friends can inadvertently become involved in the rituals and behaviours of an OCD sufferer. It may seem, at the time, the only way to help reduce the anguish that the sufferer is experiencing. By helping them with their rituals and responding to their repeated requests for reassurance, the carer is unintentionally reinforcing and strengthening the illness as opposed to challenging and overcoming it. If possible, it may be a good idea for everyone involved to sit down together every so often, to make sure everybody is on the same page with challenging the OCD rather than feeding it.

Ann, a carer, offers her experience:

> Rather than always going along with the demands of OCD (where it affects the family) it might be an idea to try and encourage ways of challenging the routines as I think the more you acknowledge them and give into them the more of a hold they will have. What works best for me is to discuss the situation with my daughter and ask her if she can see any way around it, rather than telling her what to do. Generally, making a small change that they feel they can manage works well, as to them the smallest thing will feel huge and cause great anxiety. So, give plenty of praise and encouragement. Then plant the next seed for them to think about doing something different another day.
>
> For myself, I sometimes have to say I won't be able to do one of our usual routines of going to lunch, say, because I might feel that I am in need of a break. I usually let her know in advance and we discuss beforehand that I need to do things. For me, for my own sanity, my daughter will usually accept it. She won't be happy and it will be hard for her to find an alternative but at least she understands that I need to do things for me and that I am not avoiding her or being awkward (as she will probably think and verbalise).
>
> This in turn shows her that she can cope without that particular 'lunch date with mum' and hopefully gradually by doing small things, within the family, it may help her to change, but with professional help as well.

Once you begin to change the way you respond to the demands of the illness and modify your involvement within the behaviours, hopefully the sufferer will find the strength to gain control over the OCD, rather than the OCD being in control of them.

Jay, Samantha's boyfriend, shares his thoughts on this:

> There is time as a partner you may question yourself on whether or not you are doing the right thing for your partner. Are you helping enough, are you doing enough or are you doing too much? Am I helping my partner with the condition or am I letting the condition continue without aiding my partner in recovery? This can be a thin line to walk. Just talking to your partner will help ease the tension – talking openly and honestly about what's affecting you and taking the criticism or praise they give back to you.

Be as kind and patient as possible

Irrespective of their age, or position in the family, allowing the sufferer the time, space and security they need on their recovery path will also enable them to open up and relax a little more around those closest to them. By vocalising and acknowledging to the sufferer that you accept and understand how difficult things are for them, you can show you empathise and reassure them that there is nothing they could say or do to make you stop loving or caring for them. This will give them the courage and the confidence they need to continue in the right direction. By keeping the boundary walls down between you and the sufferer, you are perpetuating the recovery cycle and creating an open, non-judgemental environment for them, which is exactly what they need to keep challenging themselves and to move forward.

Lucy says of how things at home improved, once everyone started working together:

When my family and I started to work together, it made home life so much easier. It made me understand my mum better and I think she understood me better too. We have so much more respect for each other now, which means when I want to do something like staying out later than planned or need some space, she is a lot more understanding and trusts me as well. All of this has helped me move forward with my recovery.

Find the humour

Being able to laugh together over the funny side and absurdity of the OCD thoughts and behaviours can help both you and your loved one become more detached from the disorder. Sometimes this will feel like an impossible task, but bear in mind that trying to see the lighter side of certain situations can be what gets you through them. Just make sure the sufferer feels respected and is not left out of the laughter.

Kevin, Samantha's dad, shares how finding the humour helped their relationship:

Now I laugh with Sam about her quirky ways, but what is much more important and such a huge relief is that she can now laugh at herself when she does her weird stuff.

Samantha shares:

We joke about it (OCD) a lot and laugh together, which we could never do before. Which I think has really helped us to relax with each other and find our way back together.

Keep your family routine 'normal'

Do not give up on your own everyday life or your life together with your family. Make time every week to do something you or your family particularly enjoy, together or alone. It could be listening to music, reading a book, going to the cinema, or going for a walk. Setting aside time to do your favourite activities can help relieve family tensions, whilst reinforcing the bond.

My Charlotte echoes the above:

> Going for a walk on the beach in our favourite part of the country was the best medicine for all of us; it gave us time to all breathe and be out of the everyday rut.

Remember, there is life outside of the OCD, for everyone.

What not to say

I asked some of my clients who have experienced OCD and other mental health issues to tell me some of the things their friends and family have said to them that they found unhelpful. Whilst all of the responses below are completely understandable, the manner in which they are said is often not helpful for the mindset of someone battling OCD, and they are more likely to make them feel misunderstood.

- 'Why do you always have to be like this?'
- 'Just pull yourself together.'
- 'Why can't you just be happy?'
- 'How can you be so selfish?'
- 'I can't see why you can't just ignore it.'
- 'You are blowing it out of proportion.'
- 'Stop being so weird.'

All the above phrases can potentially create a barrier between the person experiencing OCD and the person trying to help them. Getting cross and shouting will only make everyone feel worse, including you. No matter how frustrated you may be feeling, it is important to try to put those feelings aside when talking to your loved one. It is crucial not to belittle those feelings, as they will seem overwhelming to them.

What to say

It is not always easy to know what to say to someone who is struggling with a mental health issue. As my mum concurs below:

> Once I knew of the illness and then understood it was a mental illness I became very careful and wary – should I say – not to say the wrong thing, frightened of hindering the healing process that was, hopefully, taking place.

Every person has their own preferences. Here are a few ideas that you may find helpful:

- 'You can talk to me; I am listening.'
- 'This must be hard for you, but you are going to get through it.'
- 'I am there for you; you are not alone in this.'
- 'What can I do to help?'
- 'I love you.'
- 'I am so proud of you.'

A lot of the time, simply just listening can be helpful. It is important to talk to the sufferer in the same way you have always done, remembering they are the same person that they were before.

Keep communication open and positive

Communication is paramount, to enable a balance to be found between supporting your loved one and standing up to the OCD. When a family member has OCD, communications can, at times, require extra effort and patience.

Ann, mum of and carer to Aimee, says how communication helped her relationship with her daughter:

> We became closer eventually because I listened to how she was feeling and tried putting myself into her shoes, although that was very difficult. We talk a lot more now and although I still find it difficult to understand at times, we are able to discuss and try and find a solution or compromise. (But compromise is not always an option with OCD as it has such a strong hold.)

Effective communication serves as precautionary care, reassuring family members that they care about each other and appreciate each other's efforts. Good everyday communication can also make it easier to bring up issues, make requests when needed, and resolve conflict when it arises. Open, non-judgemental communication should, however, always form the basis of the approach.

Look after yourself

Supporting others can be mentally and physically exhausting. As a parent or carer, you probably spend a lot of your time focusing on everybody else, always putting everyone else's needs before your own. However, looking after your own wellbeing is just as important for you, your loved one and the whole family, as they can only be as strong as you are. You may not be able to take a break every time you need one, but it is important to have some time that is yours, whether it be going for a walk, meeting a friend, doing a relaxation class, or simply reading a book or a magazine. By doing this, it will enable you to recharge your batteries, so when you re-enter the OCD battlefield, you do so with renewed energy and focus.

Jeff Brazier, life coach, supports self-care, whilst caring for others:

> Sometimes in life we become so busy looking after everyone else that we forget to adequately care for ourselves. Regardless

of how noble the cause, the problem with this is that if all is not balanced within us as a result, our ability to tend to the needs of others is diminished as a result. We must first give to ourselves if we are going to give openly to others.

There is no definitive, right or wrong way to work together as a unit in the home; every situation, every sufferer, every family unit and every home environment is different, but by everyone sticking to the basic fundamentals and working closely together, for the benefit of everyone involved, you will be on the right path.

Chapter 10

Practical tips for carers and sufferers

After having spent the last few months working closely with all the contributors within this book, both sufferers and carers alike, and interacting with people through my social media channels, I wanted to share with you some of their thoughts on how best to navigate your way through some of the turbulent waters that you may encounter on your journey.

Listed below, in their own words, are the top 10 tips given by both carers and sufferers.

From one carer to another

1. Create a safe and supportive environment, trying to understand that the sufferer does not want to have the OCD, just as much as you do not want them to have it.
2. Be non-judgemental and listen without prejudice, no matter how difficult the situation.
3. Find someone you trust who you can talk to and open up with, so all the negative feelings do not build up inside.
4. Do not be afraid to talk about the condition; neither of you can move forward in the relationship if it is being swept under the rug.
5. Do not be afraid to seek advice. You are not going to

have all the answers or 'know how' to handle some situations so seeking some outside information or advice is important.

6. Accept that this could be a long, bumpy journey, but the destination will be worth it.
7. Be patient with the sufferer and make sure both parties are not afraid to try to laugh and make happiness instead of stress out of situations. Positivity goes a long way.
8. Accept that what the sufferer is saying is very real to them, however bizarre it sounds to you.
9. Know that even if someone does not look poorly on the outside, they may well still be really suffering on the inside.
10. Do not lose hope and never give up.

From one sufferer to another

1. Listen to yourself and your own mind. Look beyond what people expect. Really know yourself and your illness and you will find the strength to beat it.
2. Try to see things from both sides of the story, so from the sufferer's and the carer's side. It will make the relationship much more open and will allow you to communicate any worries you have with each other.
3. Be aware of your triggers. Try to eliminate these and avoid triggers from your life while you are going through the stages of recovery. They can be re-introduced when you are able to see the world without OCD goggles.
4. Be honest with others about how you are feeling.
5. Unfollow any triggering social media accounts.
6. When you go to bed, leave setbacks behind and start the new day afresh. Progress is not a linear process. You can always learn from setbacks and mistakes... look forward, not behind.

7. Try not to compare yourself with others.
8. Remind yourself that recovery does not happen overnight.
9. Look after your body as well as your mind
10. Do not give up and never lose hope.

Conclusion: From me to you...

Over the last decade I have watched my beautiful daughter, Samantha, struggle, gain control, and thankfully conquer her OCD, so I can honestly say, without hesitation, that there is a light at the end of the dark tunnel for most people living with OCD and those caring for them. This powerful and controlling mental illness was so entrenched in my daughter that I did not think it possible for her to make it out the other side... but she has. She is free from those crushing, all-consuming shackles and is now chasing her dreams, doing a degree in stage and media. In fact, by the time you read this she may have even graduated. Samantha is doing and experiencing things she herself, and none of us, ever dared to think possible. I can honestly say, she is the happiest and healthiest I have seen her for many years and every day she challenges herself, taking positive strides towards a future she now knows she has, due in large part to her utter determination and perseverance to free herself from the confines of mental illness.

I know that caring for someone with OCD can be frustrating and exhausting, and can often seem like a thankless task, but please be assured there is always a way forward. As I have mentioned over the pages of this book, each and every sufferer is unique and so is their recovery – there is no one-size-fits-all – so finding a course of treatment that is suited to them and to their loved ones is paramount. If one treatment does not work, do not be afraid to try another, and then another... It may take some time before you all find the right path to recovery, so please do not give up; you will find it, remembering always that long-term recovery is possible. Explore every avenue you can, ask the professionals as many questions as you need to, and do not settle until you are happy with the answers and choices you and your loved ones have made. Keep in mind that it is about the right recovery path, not only for the sufferer but also for the family as a whole. Mistakes will be easily made, which is only natural – I made enough of them too – but for every one made, a valuable lesson can be learnt.

Do not be afraid to stand up to the OCD by staying positive and working together to tackle it; be prepared for the long haul as any recovery takes time; acceptance and understanding are the key. Patience will need to be exercised at every turn, for everyone involved; never lose sight of the fact that the person you love is still in there, trapped by the mental illness, waiting for your help to set them free. Your focus should remain entirely on what you can do for them, not on what you cannot do for them.

There will also be times when you will need some down-time yourself, so make sure you take time out to catch up with your own friends or do something else you enjoy. Spending quality time outside of the restrictions of the OCD will help you to see things more clearly, with renewed strength and focus, ready to tackle the next challenge that your loved one will face, as every hour of every day is different.

And what of the end of the journey, when your loved one has made their recovery? Where does that leave you? I should stress here, that it is very common and completely natural to feel mixed emotions at this stage. Your life, which has previously been dominated by your loved one's illness might feel a little empty, and sometimes as their carer you may feel you have lost your own identity and direction. I know I did. At this stage, I would highly recommend thinking about life coaching sessions, as they have given me a new lease of life and enabled me to look forward to a better, brighter future, not just for Samantha but for the family as a whole.

I sincerely hope that, with each chapter, this book has helped you gain a clearer understanding of this most devastating and sometimes misunderstood mental illness and given you the hope that OCD can be conquered. Never give up; families, relationships and lives can be rebuilt. My family is living proof of that.

I will leave you with my guiding principle:

> The cure is in the recovery; there is no elevator – you have to take the stairs.

Yours with hope…
Lynn Crilly x

Samantha leaves you with her words of hope:

> I know and believe that everyone has the strength to beat their demons. It won't be easy – it will probably be one of the hardest challenges you will ever face – but one thing I can promise from the bottom of my heart is that when you come out the other side you will feel exhilarated with life, you will see beautiful things around you that you never noticed before and most of all feel an abundance of freedom and power in yourself. Trust me on this one – you will never ever regret recovery.

Resources

Charities

SANE

Website: www.sane.org.uk

Tel: 0300 304 7000 (4:30 pm – 10:30 pm daily)

SANE is a UK-wide charity working to improve quality of life for people affected by mental illness. It has three main objectives:

1. To raise awareness and combat stigma about mental illness, educating and campaigning to improve mental health services.
2. To provide care and emotional support for people with mental health problems, their families and carers, as well as information for other organisations and the public.
3. To initiate research into the causes and treatments of serious mental illness, such as schizophrenia and depression, and the psychological and social impact of mental illness.

SANE offers emotional support and information to anyone affected by mental health problems through their helpline and email services and their online Support Forum where people share their feelings and experiences.

Registered Charity Number: 296572

The Frank Bruno Foundation
Website: www.thefrankbrunofoundation.co.uk
Tel: 0800 368 8196
The Foundation aims 'to bring together the benefits of non-contact boxing with a solution-focused wellbeing programme. The aim is to bring healthy-body and healthy-mind approaches together to provide a holistic and enjoyable approach to supporting people with mental health problems. The aim is to help people to develop a healthier body and a healthier mind, building on their existing physical and emotional strengths and achievements. Our aspiration is that people will use the skills they learn on the programme to develop a happier, more fulfilling and successful future.'
Registered Charity Number: 1171012

Samaritans
Website: www.samaritans.org
Tel: +44(0)116 123
Samaritans offer a safe place for you to talk any time you like, in your own way – about whatever's getting to you. They are available round the clock, 24 hours a day, 365 days a year. If you need a response immediately, it's best to call Samaritans on the phone. This number is FREE to call.
Registered Charity Number: (England and Wales) 219432; (Scotland) SC040604.

Professionals

Steve Blacknell – TV presenter / Trainer
www.steveblacknell.com

Jeff Brazier – Life coach, NLP practitioner, TV presenter
www.jeffbraziercoaching.com

Frank Bruno MBE
Charity: www.thefrankbrunofoundation.co.uk
Website: www.frankbruno.co.uk
Twitter: Frankbrunoboxer
Facebook: Frank Bruno MBE

Dionne Curtis – Hypnotherapist, NLP practitioner, TFT practitioner, DipIPch
Website: www.whatiftherapy.co.uk
Email: dionne@whatiftherapy.co.uk
Tel: +44(0)7533149242

Angela Di Benedetto – TCM acupuncturist, Sports therapist, BSc (Hons), MBAcC, MFHT, MSST
Website: www.angiestherapies.com
Email: angie.dibe3@btinternet.com
Tel: +44(0)7779 118851

Laura Forbes – Bodytalk practitioner
Email: forbesla@icloud.com

Alison Fuller – Hypnotherapist, Reflexologist, specialising in women's health, MARR, MAR, DipIPch, CHFP, CHBP, FBM, GHR (Reg)
Website: www.thehormonaltherapist.co.uk
Email: info@thehormonaltherapist.co.uk

Catherine Kell – Child therapy and parenting support, MA(Hons), DipHyp (Paediatrics), DipClHyp, ClNLP, MNCH(Reg), CNHC (Reg)
Website: www.catherinekell.com
Email: info@catherinekell.com
Tel: +44(0)7376 388048

Kingston College of Further Education
Kingston Hall Rd, Kingston upon Thames KT1 2AQ
Email: info@kingston-college.ac.uk
Tel: +44(0)20 8546 2151

Kevin Laye – Psychotherapist and Founder of Psy-TaP, DPsy
Published author and international trainer and speaker.
Website for training: www.psy-tap.com
Website: www.kevinlaye.co.uk
Email: cameltrain@aol.com
Tel: +44(0)7803 161021
Skype: Kevin.Laye1

Liz Lisac – Integrative counsellor, MBACP (Accred), BA (Hons),
UKRCP (Registered Counsellor)
Email: liz@lisac.eu

Neil Long – NLP practitioner
Website: www.becomefree.co.uk

Mark Jermin Stage School with Charlie Brooks (Surrey and
Wales)
'A school where pupils are valued, where real confidence is born
and harnessed, and where ambitions are recognised, encouraged
and achieved.'
Website: www.markjermin.co.uk
Email: info@markjermin.co.uk
Tel: +44(0)1792 45 88 55

Kyra Mathers – Bodytalk practitioner
Email: kyra21@btinternet.com
Tel: +44(0)7739077786

Debbie Pennington – Yoga and massage specialist, CThA
Email: debcobb@hotmail.co.uk
Facebook: @yurtopiatherapies

Leanne Poyner – Personal performance and life coach
Email: leannepoyner@yahoo.com
Tel: +44(0)7868 650021

Tan Quddus – Personal trainer
Instagram: @tanqud

May Simpkin – Personalised nutrition, MSc
Website: www.maysimpkin.com
Instagram: @maysimpkinnutrition
Twitter: @MaySimpkin
Facebook: @MaySimpkinNutrition

Dave Spinx – professional actor for nearly 30 years and founder
of The Neston Drama Studio
Neston community and youth centre
Email: info@nestoncyc.co.uk
Tel: +44(0)151 336 7805

References

1. Maia TV, Cano-Colino M. The Role of Serotonin in Orbitofrontal Function and Obsessive-Compulsive Disorder. *Clinical Psychological Science* 2015; 3(3): 460–482. doi: 10.1177/2167702614566809

2. Nestadt GI, Samuels J, Riddle M, Bienvenu OJ 3rd, Liang KY, LaBuda M, Walkup J, Grados M, Hoehn-Saric R. A family study of obsessive-compulsive disorder. *Arch Gen Psychiatry* 2000; 57(4): 358-363. doi:10.1001/archpsyc.57.4.358

3. Rhéaume J, Freeston MH, Dugas MJ, Letarte H, Ladouceur R. Perfectionism, responsibility and Obsessive-Compulsive symptoms. *Behaviour Research and Therapy* 1995; 33(7): 785-794. doi: org/10.1016/0005-7967(95)00017-R

4. March JS, Franklin M, Nelson A, Foa E. Cognitive-behavioral psychotherapy for pediatric obsessive-compulsive disorder. *J Clin Child Psychol* 2001; 30: 8–18.

5. Stanford Medicine. Obsessive-compulsive and related disorders: pharmacological treatments. http://ocd.stanford.edu/treatment/pharma.html (Accessed 2 January 2018).

6. Young SN. How to increase serotonin in the human brain without drugs. *J Psychiatry Neurosci* 2007; 32(6): 394-399.

7. Penedo FJ, Dahn JR. Exercise and well-being: a review of mental and physical health benefits associated with physical activity. *Current Opinion in Psychiatry* 2005; 18(2): 189–193.

8. Lai JS, Hiles S, Bisquera A, Hure AJ, McEvoy M, Attia J. A systematic review and meta-analysis of dietary patterns and depression in community-dwelling adults. *American*

Journal of Clinical Nutrition 2014; 99(1): 181-197. doi: 10.3945/ajcn.113.069880

9. Yap K,Mogan C, Kyrios M. Obsessive-compulsive disorder and comorbid depression: The role of OCD-related and non-specific factors. *Journal of Anxiety Disorders* 2012; 26(5): 565-573.

10. Sánchez-Villegas A, Toledo E, de Irala J et al. Fast-food and commercial baked goods consumption and the risk of depression. *Public Health Nutrition* 2012; 15: 424-432.

11. www.brighttots.com/Obsessive_Compulsive_Disorder.html (Accessed 30 January 2018).

Index

Index

Index

Index

what not to say, 175
what to say, 176
tapping (meridian point)
    in Psy-Tap (psychosensory
        techniques and principles),
        70, 72, 73
    in thought field therapy, 67, 68, 69,
        71
technology, 89, 129–130
    see also internet; social media
teenagers/adolescents/young adults,
    162–166
    depression, 115
    eating disorders, 125
therapy/treatment, 19–20, 53–80
    author's experience as
        practitioner, xvii-xvii
    author's experience of seeking it
        for daughter, xiii-xvi
    recognising need for and seeking,
        42–50, 169–170
    sources, 185–188
    see also recovery
thinking and exercise, 84
thought(s)
    intrusive/worrying, 19, 28–36
    non-OCD vs OCD, 4–5
    ruminative, 27–28
thought field therapy (TFT), 67–69, 71

meridian point tapping, 67, 68, 71,
    72
threats (real or perceived), response
    to, 109
    non-OCD vs OCD, 3–6
touch in massage, 99
traditional Chinese medicine (TCM),
    101–103
treatment *see* help; therapy
triggers, 39, 180

unconscious mind, 60, 61, 62, 63, 64
Veltheim, John, 75–76
violent thoughts, 35–36
voluntary organisations, 184–185

washing (incl. hands) and cleaning, 4,
    15, 16, 18, 22, 23, 44, 46, 63–64
    children, 147, 153
    treatment targeting, 56, 171
wellbeing, 81–104
workplace, 150–151
worrying/intrusive thoughts, 19,
    28–36

yoga, 91–93
young adults *see* teenagers/
    adolescents/young adults

eNewsletter & Carers Workshops

To subscribe to my monthly newsletter 'Hope with Mental Health' or to find out about our upcoming carers workshops. Please email: contact@lynncrilly.co.uk.

Visit my website: https://lynncrilly.com.

YouTube Channel

Subscribe to our Youtube channel 'Hope with Mental Health' for weekly vlogs discussing anything and everything mental health.

Link:
http://www.youtube.com/c/HopewithMentalHealth

Trouble Muncher

Created and developed by Samantha Crilly
to help people dissociate from their negative
thoughts, the Trouble Muncher® is a FREE, fun
and friendly app which uses quirky sound and
graphics to encourage users to live life with a lot
less worry.

The Trouble Muncher® appears quirky, however,
it features a leading edge psychological technique
– Neuro-linguistic Programming (NLP), which if
mastered, may significantly reduce the users worry.

You can download the app 'Trouble Muncher' for
iOS or Android in the app stores.

Coming soon...

Hope with Eating Disorders
Second edition

By Lynn Crilly

Hammersmith Health Books is delighted to announce the second edition of Lynn Crilly's acclaimed guide for families and friends of people with eating disorders.

'Written from first-hand experience, Lynn's perspective is an invaluable addition to the writing about eating disorders.'
Professor Janet Treasure, OBE PhD FRCP FRCPsych

'As a parent, I feel Lynn's book is an essential guide and support for anyone concerned about their son's or daughter's eating habits, self-esteem and general wellbeing.'
Bobby Davro – entertainer

'As a former sufferer myself of what is still considered a bit of a taboo subject, I found this book delivers information in a friendly, easy to understand way, making you want to read on.'
Suzanne Dando, Olympic gymnast

'Lynn's passion and determination to help people whose lives are affected by eating disorders is inspiring.'
Jo Swinson, MP

'Essential reading for anyone you truly wished to understand what it is like living with an eating disorder.'
Lord John Prescott